MW00776949

Sunscreens – Biohazard 2

Proof of Toxicity Keeps Piling Up

Breaking Away from the
MASS CONSciousness Series:
Insights Beyond Tunnel Vision

Elizabeth Plourde, Ph.D.
Marcus Plourde, Ph.D.

Other titles by Elizabeth Plourde:

Sunscreens – Biohazard: Treat as Hazardous Waste

Sunscreens – Biohazard: Diet and Guide to Safe Sunning

EMF Freedom: Solutions for the 21st Century Pollution

Your Guide to Hysterectomy, Ovary Removal, & Hormone Replacement: What ALL Women Need to KNOW

Hysterectomy? The Best or Worst Thing that Ever Happened to Me? A Collection of Women's Personal Experiences

PUBLISHER'S NOTE
AN IMPORTANT CAUTION TO OUR READERS:

This book is not a medical manual and cannot take the place of personalized medical advice and treatment from a qualified physician. The reader should regularly consult a physician in matters relating to his or her health, particularly with respect to any symptoms that may require diagnosis or treatment. Although certain medical professionals are mentioned in this book, no endorsement, warranty or guarantee by the author is intended. Every attempt has been made to ensure that the information contained in this book is current, however, due to the fact that research is ongoing, some of the material may be invalidated by new findings. The author and publisher cannot guarantee that the information and advice in this book are safe and proper for every reader. For that reason, this book is sold without warranties or guarantees of any kind, expressed or implied, and the author and publisher disclaim any liability, loss or damage caused by the contents. If you do not wish to be bound by these cautions and conditions, you may return your copy to the publisher for a full refund.

Plourde, Elizabeth
Plourde, Marcus
Sunscreens – Biohazard 2: Proof of Toxicity Keeps Piling Up

ISBN: 978-0-9913688-5-3
LCCN: 2018911592

Published by: 21st Century Health Consulting LLC
                dba New Voice Publications
                publisher@newvoice.net
                Irvine, CA 92604

Dedication

We dedicate this book to all who read these truths, act on them, and pass them on to all the people throughout the world.

Acknowledgements

Thank you to the many researchers around the globe who are not being hampered by what has become accepted as truth: "Sunscreens are essential to prevent skin cancers." Thanks to your time and effort this statement will be another harmful myth that becomes debunked, just as with cigarettes and DDT.

♥ *Elizabeth Plourde, Ph.D.*
Marcus Plourde, Ph.D.

TABLE OF CONTENTS

Dedication   v
Acknowledgements   vii
List of Tables and Figures   xiii
List of Abbreviations   xv
Preface – *Sunscreens Biohazard* – 2012   xvii
Preface – *Sunscreens Biohazard 2* – 2019   xix

1 Introduction   **23**
    Key points discussed in this book   23
    Sunscreen's Impact on the Systems of the Body   24
    Melanoma – U.S. Incidence Rates between 1975 & 2015   26
    The Benefits of Melanin   27
    Levels of Skin Penetration by UVB Solar Rays   28
    Levels of Skin Penetration by UVA Solar Rays   29
    Levels of Skin Penetration by IR Solar Rays   30
    Sun Causing Melanoma or Sunscreens Preventing It
       Was Never Proven!   31

2 Chemical and Physical UV Filters   **37**
    The Chemistry of Sunscreens   37
    Chemical Filters   38
    Benzophenone-3 (BP3)   39
    The Benzophenone HMB   43
    Cinnamates: OMC and OC   44
    Methoxycinnamate (OMC)   44
    Octocrylene (OC)   44
    Avobenzone   44
    Camphors   45
    Estrogenic Sunscreen Chemicals   46
    Body Penetration   47
    Additive Effect   50

3 Titanium Dioxide (TiO2) and Zinc Oxide (ZnO)   51
Bulk vs. Nano Particles (NPs)   54
Particle Sizes Found In Sunscreen Powders   55
The Great Expectations Held for DDT have Been
          Realized   57
Differing Forms of TiO2 – Create
          Slightly Differing Harms   58
Rutile and Anastase Explanation   58
Zinc Oxide (ZnO)   59
Aluminum   60
Spray Sunscreens – Do Not Breathe Them In   61

**4 Reproduction: Detrimental For Both Expectant
          Mothers and Their Fetuses   63**
Females – Beware of Food Products and Cosmetics that
          Contain TiO2 Nanoparticles   66
Fetal Development   66

**5 Hormonal Disruptions: Creating Gender Bending or
          Gender Dysphoria   71**

6 How Sunscreens Are Detrimental to Our Health   75
They Generate Reactive Oxygen Species – ROS   75
Inflammation   76
Heart, Liver, and Immune Function   77
Thyroid Disruption   78
Cancer   79
Breast Cancer   79
Prostate Cancer   80
More Solar Radiation = Less Multiple Myeloma   80
Leaky Gut and Disrupted Microbiome   80
Mitochondrial Dysfunction   81
Mitochondrial Dysfunction Diseases   82
Diabetes   83
NPs Breach the Body's Built-in Protective Barriers   84
Blood-brain Barrier (BBB) Compromised   84
Brain   84
Neurotoxicity to the Central Nervous System (CNS)   85
Mental Health   85

7 DNA Damage – Alteration of Genomes on the Planet   **87**
Changes In Gene Expressions – Impairs the Body's
    Ability to Detox   87
Octocrylene (OC) Creates 100s of DNA Alterations   87
ZnO NPs Alter DNA   87
MTHFR Genes Altered by TiO_2, ZnO, and BP3   88

8 Swimming Pools – Now Toxic, Poison Filled
**   Chemical Dumps**   **91**

9 Vitamin D and Sunshine's Multiple Health Benefits   **93**
Sunshine Enhances   96
Obesity – Obesogens   97
Cholesterol Sulfate   98
TiO_2 Adsorbs Flame Retardants = Increasing
    Cellular Intake   98

10 Sunscreens' Ecological Harm to the Environment   **101**
Coral Damage   102
The Beginnings of Change - Making a Difference   106

11 Future Warnings – New Ideas Being Considered
**   Will Cause Harm as Well**   **107**

12 Antioxidants: Mother Nature's Safe and
**   Natural Protective Sunscreens**   **109**
Just one antioxidant example: Garlic   110
Conclusions   110

Resources – Newsletter   113
Resources – EMF Radiation Information and Remediation   114
Resources – EMF Products   115
Resources – Scientific Methods   116
Appendix A: Protecting Yourself – Naturally   117
Appendix B: Synonyms for Benzophenone-3   127
Picture Credits   129
References   131
Index   157
About the Authors   165

List of Tables and Figures

Tables

Table 1: Melanoma – U.S. Incidence Rates between
1975 and 2015   26
Table 2: Particle Sizes Found In Sunscreen Powders:
Used for Sunscreen Formulations   55
Table 3: UV Index Rating System   120

Figures

Figure 1: Sunscreen's Impact on the Systems of the Body   24
Figure 2: Levels of Skin Penetration by UVB Solar Rays   28
Figure 3: Levels of Skin Penetration by UVA Solar Rays   29
Figure 4: Levels of Skin Penetration by IR Solar Rays   30
Figure 5: Human Epidermal Cells with Internalized
TiO_2 Nanoparticles   52
Figure 6: Summary of Neurotoxicity of Aluminum   60
Figure 7: Vitamin D Impacts the Body in Many Ways   94
Figure 8: Low Vitamin D Status   97
Figure 9: Coral Samples Die Within 96 Hours
after Exposure   103

List of Abbreviations

	Wavelength Range	Solar Spectrum Description
IR	Infrared radiation wavelengths	
IRA	Infrared A radiation wavelengths	700 – 1,400 nm
IRB	Infrared B radiation wavelengths	1,400 – 3,000 nm
IRC	Infrared C radiation wavelengths	3,000 nm – 1 mm
IU	International Units	
mcg	microgram	
μg/L	micrograms/liter	
mm	millimeter	
ng/mL	nanograms/milliliter	
nm	nanometer	

TiO_2 Titanium dioxide

UV Ultraviolet radiation wavelengths

UVC =	Ultraviolet C radiation wavelengths	100 – 280 nm
UVB =	Ultraviolet B radiation wavelengths	280 – 315 nm
UVA =	Ultraviolet A radiation wavelengths	315 – 400 nm

ZnO   Zinc oxide

Preface – *Sunscreens Biohazard* – 2012

While spending time in Hawaii in the summer of 2010, I saw headlines in their newspaper saying "Coral Reefs Dying Due to Global Warming". This did not make sense to me as I have been swimming in Hawaiian waters for over 40 years and this year was the first summer that I had to coax myself into the water, one inch at a time, because it was so cool. I have been a medical researcher and author of health books for 20 years and decided to start investigating why the coral would die; it certainly was not due to warmer water temperatures. When I immediately uncovered an article that unequivocally demonstrated that coral die just from exposure to sunscreen chemicals, I knew I had to write a book to start warning the world that sunscreens were jeopardizing the beautiful coral reefs of the world. It is not only coral, it is the whole marine habitat that is threatened as many fish and species of marine life depend on the coral.

I had no idea at the time that I would uncover the importance of the biochemistry training that I had experienced to become a California licensed Clinical Laboratory Scientist (CLS), as well as my 20 years of being a medical researcher on hormones and hormone balancing.

As I uncovered the impact these sunscreens are having not only on coral, but fish and birds as well, I began to be horrified at how life itself on the Earth is being threatened. Then when I found studies that showed these sunscreen chemicals are in the blood of almost 100% of ALL Americans, including the ones who state they have never used a sunscreen, I realized if fish and birds are being reproductively impacted, then humans exposed to these chemicals must be too. Our babies could start exhibiting some of the same problems that scientists are discovering in most all of the life forms they are testing with sunscreen exposure.

I also had no concept of the ubiquitousness and pervasiveness of so many products on the market today that now have sunscreen chemicals in addition to those dedicated as sunscreens. In fact, it is almost impossible to find products without them.

I became even more dedicated to this work when I realized that vitamin D deficiency diseases (e.g., rickets), all but wiped out a century ago, have been returning due to the encouraged behavior to shield against sunshine. The body needs the sun's rays in order to manufacture its essential vitamin D within the skin.

Thank you for caring enough to pick up this book. Please care enough about the planet and your family and friends to get multiple copies of it and pass them on to as many people as possible. If we stop buying products with sunscreen chemicals, they should stop making them.

Thank you for sharing the journey of protecting our home, the planet Earth, and protecting your families and friends,

— *Elizabeth Plourde, Ph.D.* – 2012

Preface – *Sunscreens Biohazard 2* – 2019

In the fall of 2017, I was asked to write a sunscreen article for a health journal. Since my original sunscreen book was published in 2012, I decided to look at the latest research to update the information that I would incorporate in the article. I know that I was concerned enough about the truth regarding sunscreens to write my first book, but seeing how the latest research confirmed my fears over the amount of toxicity of sunscreens and revealed they were even far worse than my earlier research revealed; I knew it had to become a second volume of the truth about sunscreens and how they harm all life on the planet. Please hear these truths:

Sunscreens do not reduce melanomas or skin cancers.
All the FDA approved chemicals harm our bodies, our children, and all life on the planet.
Sunscreens now contaminate all water sources.

Thank you for reading this information. Please tell everyone you meet, as everyone deserves the truth regarding how these toxic chemicals are impacting both them and their children's health, as we have been led to believe many misconceptions when it comes to sunscreens and the sun's impact on humanity.

— *Elizabeth Plourde, Ph.D.* – 2019

Sunscreens – Biohazard 2

Proof of Toxicity Keeps Piling Up

Breaking Away from the
MASS CONSciousness Series:
Insights Beyond Tunnel Vision

Chapter 1
Introduction

Key points discussed in this book:

- Researchers claim no solid proof sunshine causes melanoma or that sunscreens prevent it.
- As a result of sunscreen use, melanoma incidence has climbed since they were introduced.
- All sunscreen chemicals are hormone (endocrine) disruptors – reproductive and thyroid hormones.
- Sunscreen chemicals create body-wide alterations that compromise our long-term health.
- Swimming pools have become a sea of toxic *chlorine altered* sunscreen chemicals.
- The sun creates vitamin D3 in our skin that prevents cancers, including skin cancers, and many other disabling conditions.

I am truly saddened that the book I researched and published in 2012: *Sunscreens Biohazard: Treat as Hazardous Waste* has made little impact on the world-wide production, proliferation, and use of sunscreens. If anything, the continued promotion of their necessity "to protect us from harmful solar radiation" has continued with ever increasing pressure. My background in biochemistry and intense years of hormone research allowed the opportunity for me to see the potential hormonal damage that would be caused by these many endocrine (hormonally) disruptive chemicals that are utilized in ALL sunscreens products. They interfere with normal functioning, normal development, and the ability to reproduce for many species of life on our planet.

The sunscreens are included in an article that is looking at the increasing numbers of environmental contaminants found in living beings. They expressed their concern: " . . . however, the adverse effects of environmental exposure on the general population are largely unknown. . . . The most prevalent emerging contaminants include perfluorinated compounds (fluorine-carbon compounds for stains, sunscreens, water, and stick-resistant coatings), water disinfection by-products, gasoline additives, manufactured nanomaterials, human and veterinary pharmaceuticals, and UV-filters [sunscreens]." Figure 1 below shows how they view these contaminants and how they are impacting all of life. All of the conditions listed in this figure are detailed throughout this book as studies continue to reveal that sunscreen chemicals impact every organ and bodily function.

Sunscreen's Impact on the Systems of the Body

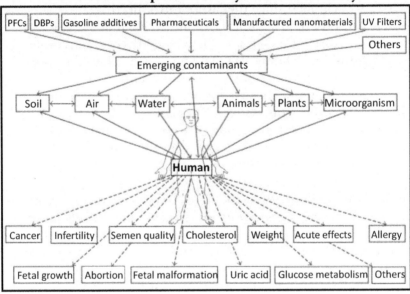

Figure 1.

Source: Lei M, Zhang L, Lei J, et al. Overview of emerging contaminants and associated human health effects. *Biomed Res Int.* 2015;2015:404796. Reprinted with permission.

The human body is so well designed that it is *total sunshine,* which includes both UVB and UVA, and the vitamin D3 that the body creates in the skin upon exposure to sunlight that protects the balance necessary to keep skin cells from becoming cancerous.

In other words, the use of sunscreens blocks the body's ability to protect itself. This is demonstrated by the fact that both melanoma and non-melanoma (squamous and basal cell cancers) have risen dramatically since sunscreens were introduced. Sunscreens were introduced in the 1970s, yet here we are almost 50 years later with the incidence of melanoma having undergone staggering increases over this last half century.

In the United States, the 1970 incidence rate for melanoma was 5.7 per 100,000.[1] Between 2003 to 2012, the incidence rate of melanoma kept increasing significantly. For white men, it steadily increased at 1.7% per year, and for women the increase was 1.4% per year over the 10 years the statistics were gathered. This means that the incidence of melanoma increased 17% for men and 14% for women just in this 10-year period. It remained level among men with increased brown pigment (melanin) in their skin, i.e.: black, Hispanic, American Indian, and Asian men; as melanin is the best solar protector our skin can have.[2]

These rapidly increasing cancer rates have translated into a 200% increase between 1973 and 2011.[3] The increase is even higher when looking at children and white female young adults. Their incidence since 1973 has increased 253%.[4]

The following chart shows the increase in incidence over the period of time of sunscreen use based on the statistics that are available today.

Melanoma – U.S. Incidence Rates between 1975 and 2015

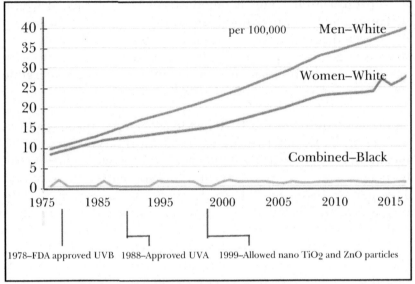

Table 1. Melanoma incidence rates since sunscreens were approved by the Food and Drug Administration (FDA).

Sources: NIH National Cancer Institute Website. Cancer Statistics: Fast Facts. Retrieved September 18, 2018 from: www.seer. cancer.gov/faststats/selections.php?

The Benefits of Melanin

Black skin has several factors that protect from skin cancers. Just one of them is melanin, which acts as a filter that reduces all wavelengths of light equally, providing so much protection that five times more ultraviolet light, which includes both UVB and UVA, reaches the upper layer (dermis) of skin of Caucasians compared to blacks.[5]

This protection provided by melanin is why whiter skin tans on exposure to sunlight. The melanin that creates the tan is nature's sun absorber, which protects the skin naturally. Rather than fear it, realize tanning is the body's way of providing cancer protection for the skin. Building up a tan slowly is great protection.

If sunscreens worked, this chart would be going in the opposite direction, and yet melanoma is not showing a decreasing incidence, only just steadily increasing numbers since sunscreens were introduced. This climb makes total sense, as research has proven the interference that sunscreens create in the skin makes the person more vulnerable to the development of both melanoma and non-melanoma skin cancers. To understand why, we have to look at the basic concept of how sunscreens work. **In reality, the entire concept of ultraviolet protection is wrong!** Only 4% of the entire solar radiation spectrum is the ultraviolet (UV) radiation that is blocked in the highly recommended broad spectrum sunscreens. Yes, you are blocking the UVB radiation that causes the sunburn, which is what the original sunscreens did when they were approved by the Food and Drug Administration (FDA) in 1978. So for the first ten years, FDA approved sunscreens only blocked UVB. The following diagram shows the level of penetration of the UVB rays in the skin. They are what cause the typical sunburn.

Levels of Skin Penetration by UVB Solar Rays

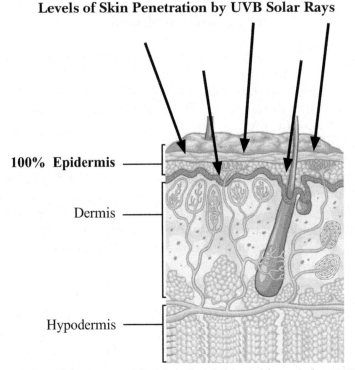

Figure 2.   Skin penetration levels of the epidermis by UVB
           radiation.

Source: Plourde E. *Sunscreens – Biohazard: Treat as Hazardous Waste*. New
       Voice Publications. 2012.

The increasing incidence in melanoma reveals that UVB blocking
sunscreens that stopped the sunburn were definitely not studied enough before they were brought to market. Blocking only
UVB allows in the UVA, which actually creates more melanoma.
The diagram below shows how much deeper the UVA rays enter
the skin, compared to UVB. In 1988 the FDA, recognizing this,
made the regulation that sunscreens had to include UVA block-
age as well as UVB. Sunscreens that block both UVB and UVA
radiation are referred to as *broad spectrum* sunscreens.

Levels of Skin Penetration by UVA Solar Rays

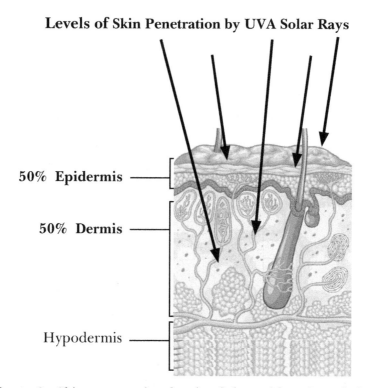

50% **Epidermis** ——

50% **Dermis** ——

Hypodermis ——

Figure 3. Skin penetration levels of the epidermis and dermis by UVA radiation.

Source: Plourde E. *Sunscreens – Biohazard. Treat as Hazardous Waste*. New Voice Publications. 2012.

The remaining solar radiations are visible wavelengths (49%), while 47% are near infrared (NIR) radiation that is subdivided into infrared A (IRA), infrared B (IRB), and infrared C (IRC). The diagram on the next page shows how much deeper the NIR rays go into our skin, allowing them to enter structures inside the skin where they cause damage. So far, nothing put on the skin can stop these deeply penetrating wavelengths.

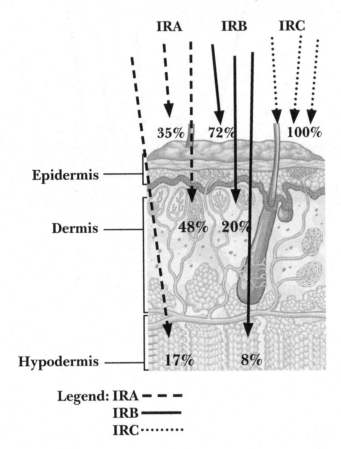

Figure 4. Skin penetration of epidermis, dermis, and hypodermis
      by IRA, IRB, and IRC radiation.

Source: Plourde E. *Sunscreens – Biohazard: Treat as Hazardous Waste*. New
      Voice Publications. 2012.

This deep penetration damage leads to all types of skin cancer.
As a result of using sunscreens that prevent sunburns, people are
in the sun many times longer than normal because their skin is
blocked from providing its red warning light – the sunburn. It
is as if the wire to the red warning light on the dash of the car

telling the driver there is a problem under the hood has been cut. The skin can no longer warn that it is time to get out of the sun. Our skin burns when our body has run out of our natural protective nutrients (antioxidants) that prevent skin damage from the sun. The burn is our red warning light – further sun exposure will cause skin damage – it is the signal telling us it is time to cover up or get out of the sun.

> For decades now, we have blocked the warning light and have sat in the NIR radiation, far longer as a result of the false sense of security that we are protected, unaware of the solar radiation damage that is going on deep inside the skin.

Sun Causing Melanoma or Sunscreens Preventing It Was Never Proven!

Studies were published in the 1980s and 1990s stating that it was **NOT PROVEN THAT SUNSHINE CAUSED MELANOMA, OR SKIN CANCERS.** In 1989, the Council on Scientific Affairs published: "There also is much circumstantial evidence that the increase in the incidence of cutaneous malignant melanoma during the past half century is related to increased sun exposure, but this has not been proven." Their recommended ". . . safety measures include: (1) minimizing exposure to ultraviolet radiation, (2) being aware of reflective surfaces while in the sun, (3) wearing protective clothing, (4) avoiding use of artificial tanning devices, and (5) protecting infants and children."[6]

In 1994 researchers utilizing three different sunscreen chemicals: the cinnamate octinoxate (OMC), octyl-N-dimethyl-p-aminobenzoate (a PABA), and benzophenone-3 (BP3) on mice, found: "However, the **SUNSCREENS FAILED TO PROTECT AGAINST UV RADIATION-INDUCED INCREASE IN MELANOMA INCIDENCE."** . . . "The sunscreens or vehicle alone did not significantly alter tumor growth. Conclusions: Protection against

sunburn does not necessarily imply protection against other possible UV radiation effects, such as enhanced melanoma growth.
Implications: Sunscreen protection against UV radiation-induced
inflammation may encourage prolonged exposure to UV radiation and thus may actually increase the risk of melanoma development. These findings suggest that further research on the ability of sunscreens to prevent melanoma is urgently needed."[7]

This study published in the *Journal of the National Cancer Institute*
sparked a series of correspondence letters in the journal. It was
challenged by doctors who were funded by grants from cosmetic
and pharmaceutical companies (sunscreen manufacturers) who
wrote into the journal complaining about the wording, claiming
the public could be misled by how they were reporting their
results.[8]

As part of the correspondence other researchers wrote: "As with
melanoma, we have not been able to find any epidemiological
study that presents results that are supportive of the usual
assumption that sunscreens prevent basal cell carcinoma. On
the contrary, women who used sunscreens in a large cohort
[exposed compared to controls] study had higher incidence
rates of basal cell carcinoma than nonusers." These investigators
found a higher incidence of basal cell carcinoma with sunscreen
use, and stated their findings do not support that sunscreens
prevent basal cell carcinoma.[9] And, saying "as with melanoma"
they found study results that do not support sunscreens prevent
melanoma.

The study's researchers stated: "To date, there are no data on
humans that permit us to deduce what role or roles solar radiation
has in cutaneous melanoma. . . . Thus, assumptions about the
potential beneficial or detrimental effects of sunscreen use for
melanoma incidence or mortality in humans are premature, and
claims on either side are inappropriate."[10]

Others responded with: "**. . . the scientific rationale for a recommendation to use chemical sunscreens as a tool to prevent skin cancer still is not supported by the existing evidence. Instead, it now seems appropriate to question whether sunscreens are effective in preventing either melanoma or basal cell carcinoma in humans. Pending further studies, it may be wiser to temporarily withhold recommendations to use chemical sunscreens in preference to more traditional alternatives . . .**"[11]

> The traditional alternatives include use of hats, and clothing, and common sense about how long your skin will allow you to be in the sun before damage occurs.

Research over the years still has not proven that sunscreens prevent skin cancer. A study appeared in a 2009 *Dermatologic Clinics* stating: "This article reviews the research on, and examines the epidemiology and prevention of melanoma. Despite the great quantity of research into environmental and genetic causes, and the ease of diagnosis, incidence and mortality have risen in all developed countries during the last half century [since sunscreens were introduced]." They concluded: **"It is still not clear that sunscreens of any sort will provide protection from developing melanoma."** . . . **"No conclusion could be drawn about the cancer-preventive activity of topical use of sunscreens against basal-cell carcinoma and cutaneous melanoma."** . . . **"Protection from UV radiation exposure–shade seeking, staying out of the sun during the peak hours of UV radiation, and wearing protective clothing–is likely to be effective."**[12]

Indeed, research on non-melanoma skin cancer incidences confirms these findings. The incidence of non-melanoma skin cancer has steadily increased in Australia. The incidence in 1985 was 555 per 100,000, a rate that climbed to 2,448 per 100,000 in 2011.[13]

The public promotion of staying out of the sun and using sunscreen, has resulted in a 2017 article in *International Journal of Environmental Research and Public Health* stating: **"Others are so mortally afraid of the sun that they use protective creams that contain ecologically harmful substances such as endocrine disruptors or nano-sized metal oxides, the ecosystem fate and effect of which have not been sufficiently studied."**[14]

A 2017 study also identified sunscreens have been insufficiently studied when researchers concluded: "Unfortunately, the effects of repeated, long-term and low-dose exposures to single compounds and mixtures of various UV filters is also poorly studied."[15]

Thirty years after FDA approval, a 2007 study determined that blocking only UVB, allowing in large quantities of UVA actually increases the risk of melanoma for populations above 40 degrees latitude around the globe.[16] This means that in almost all of Europe and the United States, from approximately Denver north, the sunscreens have not been protective, which is one reason melanomas have experienced such increases in incidence.

A 2011 study of people who wore sunscreens versus people who sought shade and wore a hat and long sleeves found they had fewer sunburns and concluded avoiding the sun on the skin is more effective than the use of sunscreen.[17]

Why weren't these studies carried out before the promotion of the false promise that sunscreen can prevent melanoma was mass marketed to the entire world? There were published studies that revealed these chemicals could cause hormone disruption, but they were not brought to the attention of the public.

The mass promotion of sunscreens is very financially lucrative and therefore difficult to overcome the ubiquitous advertising that permeates the world that: "They are essential for any sun exposure." The American market in 2014 produced $1.5 billion in revenues, while in Europe the market brought in $2.2 billion for the year.[18] **Manufacturers do not want to give up such lucrative revenues.** This leads to many research studies being funded by pharmaceutical or cosmetic companies showing there is no harm from these chemicals. Yet, nothing could be further from the truth.

How could a multi-billion-dollar industry that affects all life on the planet and promoted as necessary to prevent melanoma have been only *poorly studied*, or without having been *sufficiently studied*, as to the effect on the Earth's ecosystem, long-term exposure, or testing combinations of the chemicals that make them more toxic, before world-wide mass advertising and promotion? This lack of proper research now has resulted in all the waters of the world being contaminated – harming all marine life and our human lives.

> The entire body is being harmed, causing damage that may be irreversible – impacting this and future generations.

Chapter 2
Chemical and Physical UV Filters

We need to review the science of each individual chemical that
has been approved by the FDA. At least one of the chemicals
outlined in this chapter "has to be included" in a formulation
to earn a solar protective rating factor (SPF) for the ability to
sell it as a sunscreen. As you read through this section, you will
notice a common thread developing: ALL of these chemical are
creating detrimental harm. At one time, we believed zinc oxide
in the white pasty form was the least harmful, but research is
finding it also causes harm.

There are two point to be gained from this chapter:
1. All the FDA approved chemicals are detrimental to the
   body and the environment.
2. These chemicals have been tested individually and not
   tested in the formulations offered, which combining any
   chemical creates a new chemical with its own actions and
   reactions. In other words, there is nothing that can be
   purchased that has been tested sufficiently to earn the
   right to be classified as safe.

The Chemistry of Sunscreens
There are two main types of filters that have been promoted as
having the ability to block ultraviolet (UV) radiation from penetrating the skin. Chemical filters (BP3, OMC, etc.) absorb the
ultraviolet rays. Physical filters, titanium dioxide (TiO_2) and
zinc oxide (ZnO), scatter and reflect UV rays. Animal as well as
human studies identify that these agents impair both hormonal
and developmental pathways, making researchers urge that the
safety and regulation of sunscreens must be reviewed and **alternative types of protection from solar radiation need to be
developed.**

There are 16 filters approved by the U.S. FDA that are allowed to be used as a sunscreen in the U.S.A. They and the concentrations that are allowed are:

> Aminobenzoic acid (PABA) (15%),
> Avobenzone (3%),
> Cinoxate (3%),
> Dioxybenzone (benzophenone-8) (3%),
> Homosalate (15%),
> Menthyl anthranilate (not permitted in Europe or Japan) (5%),
> Octocrylene (OC) (10%),
> Octyl methoxycinnamate (octinoxate, OMC) (7.5%),
> Octyl salicylate (octisalate) (5%),
> Oxybenzone (BP3) (6%),
> Padimate O (8%),
> Phenylbenzimidazole sulfonic acid (ensulizole) (4%),
> Sulisobenzone (BP4) (10%),
> Titanium dioxide (TiO$_2$) (25%),
> Trolamine salicylate (12%),
> Zinc oxide (ZnO) (25%).

Only 8 are used regularly due to problems with the others (i.e., like turning the skin blue on exposure to UV light). The 8 are oxybenzone, avobenzone, octinoxate, octisalate, homosalate, octocrylene, titanium dioxide, and zinc oxide. Only 2 of these are believed to also provide filtering for UVA. They are avobenzone and zinc oxide. Avobenzone primarily filters UVA, zinc oxide is used because it filters UVB as well as UVA.[19]

Chemical Filters
Chemical filters are endocrine or hormone disruptors. There are three main classes of chemicals that are used. They are benzophenones, camphors, and cinnamates. Structurally they mimic the shape of our natural hormones, so they are capable of binding to the body's hormone receptors. By blocking the ability of natural hormones to sit in their receptors, they disrupt our delicately balanced and perfectly tuned hormones that create our body, our ability to reproduce, our ability to maintain good health,

and energy for living (i.e., like our thyroid hormones). Endocrine disrupters (EDs) alter normal hormonal regulation by increasing or decreasing effects on our cells' hormone receptors. They block the body's normal reproductive hormones by binding to estrogen or testosterone receptors. In other words, they are imposters taking the place of our vital to life hormones – impeding their ability to function and keep us healthy. These false endocrines can alter reproductive function, which can cause feminization. They also bind to the thyroid receptors, and may disrupt the nervous and neuroendocrine system. Their interferences can disrupt our immune system, our behavior, and affect our memory.

Mammals, fish, birds, reptiles, amphibians and aquatic invertebrates all show effects from these sunscreen endocrine disruptions. Scientists are studying them due to their concern about the long-term effects of these endocrine disruptors, since traces of not only sunscreen agents but also plastics, brominated fire retardants and cosmetic ingredients are now widely distributed throughout the environment and found in humans in their blood and urine.[20]

Other researchers confirm this stating: "The potential adverse effects induced by UV-filters in experimental animals include reproductive/developmental toxicity and disturbance of hypothalamic-pituitary-thyroid axis (HPT axis)."[21] **This means all of our major hormone organs are impacted by these sunscreen chemicals.**

Benzophenone-3 (BP3)
Please see Appendix B for the list of the at least 40 different synonyms for BP3 that can also be listed on the label of sunscreen and cosmetic products.

All chemicals are researched in regards to their safety and/or toxicity. The findings are made available in what is called a Material Safety Data Sheet (MSDS). The MSDS for benzophenone lists many warnings that should give us pause that this class of chemical was ever even considered to be slathered on our skin on a daily basis. Right at the top of the sheet it states:

> "**Caution!** May cause eye and skin irritation. May cause respiratory and digestive tract irritation. The toxicological properties of this material have not been fully investigated.
>
> **Chronic:** Animal feeding studies have resulted in liver and bone marrow damage.
>
> **Handling:** Use with adequate ventilation. Avoid contact with eyes, skin, and clothing. Avoid ingestion and inhalation.
>
> **Storage:** Store in a tightly closed container. Keep from contact with oxidizing materials. [The sun is an oxidizer; why did they not heed this warning?].
>
> **Skin:** Wear appropriate gloves to prevent skin exposure.
>
> **Clothing:** Wear appropriate protective clothing to prevent skin exposure.
>
> **Epidemiology: No data available.**
>
> **Teratogenicity**: **No data available**
> [Disruption of fetal development with possible birth defects].
>
> **Reproductive effects: No data available.**
>
> **Mutagenicity: No data available.**
> **Neurotoxicity: No data available.**
> [We have been told to use it continually, and wear it in all the waterways, yet there was no testing as to whether the chemical was harmful to fetuses or the ability to reproduce, the possibility of causing cancers, or of harming our neurological pathways.]
>
> **Environmental:** Benzophenone will have low to medium soil mobility category. Leaching in soil should be important; benzophenone has been detected in groundwater samples."[22]

These statements clearly show it has **NOT** been researched before being unleashed on all life on the planet.

As part of the United States National Biomonitoring Program, the Centers for Disease Control (CDC) Environment Fact Sheet (April 7, 2017) for benzophenone-3 includes:

Benzophenone-3 (BP-3) Factsheet

"Benzophenone-3 (BP-3) is a naturally occurring chemical found in some flowering plants. BP-3 absorbs and scatters the sun's harmful ultraviolet (UV) rays. For this reason, it is produced for use as sunscreen in lotions, conditioners, and cosmetics. BP-3 also is used in plastic products to block and prevent UV rays from altering the plastic and the contents inside.

People may be exposed to BP-3 when they apply sunscreen or cosmetic products that contain the chemical to their skin. Once applied, a small amount of BP-3 passes through the skin into the body.

The human health effects from skin exposure to low levels of BP-3 are unknown. BP-3 has been shown to cause weak hormonal activity in laboratory animals. More research is needed to assess the human health effects of exposure to BP-3.

In the Fourth National Report on Human Exposure to Environmental Chemicals (Fourth Report), CDC scientists measured BP-3 in the urine of 2,517 participants aged six years and older who took part in the National Health and Nutrition Examination Survey (NHANES) during 2003–2004. By measuring BP-3 in urine, scientists can estimate the amount of BP-3 that has entered people's bodies.

CDC scientists found BP-3 in the urine of nearly all of the people tested, indicating widespread exposure to BP-3 in the U.S. population.

Finding a measurable amount of BP-3 in urine does not imply that levels of BP-3 cause an adverse health effect. Biomonitoring studies on levels of BP-3 provide physicians and public health officials with reference values so they can determine whether people have been exposed to higher levels of BP-3 than are found in the general population. Biomonitoring data can also help scientists plan and conduct research on exposure and health effects."[23]

This clearly shows insufficient research of BP3 regarding its potential toxicity, yet they still continue to utilize BP3 and strongly promote its use. BP3 is not a chemical that is found naturally in the body, therefore there should be no *standard* or *normal* amount found in the body, yet after decades of use it is now found in almost everyone who has been tested for it, because it is now in our water systems.

Assuming that the only source of BPs is from sunscreens, Danish researchers thought the BPs would only show up in school children in the summer. In order to find out, they monitored kindergartners' urine to determine total exposure to sunscreen chemicals. On finding that even in winter, when they did not use sunscreen, the children excreted metabolites of benzophenones, they expressed concern that sources of the chemicals may be due from unintended consequences, with no benefit, and could be potentially harmful.[24]

Studies like these show how the sunscreen chemicals have permeated our environment.

This chemical is not just in sunscreens:

> "Benzophenone is used as a flavor ingredient, a fragrance enhancer, a perfume fixative and an additive for plastics, coatings and adhesive formulations; it is also used in the manufacture of insecticides, agricultural chemicals, hypnotic drugs, antihistamines and other pharmaceuticals. Benzophenone is used as an ultraviolet (UV)-curing agent in sunglasses, and to prevent UV light from damaging scents and colors in products such as perfumes and soaps. Moreover, it can be added to plastic packaging as a UV blocker, which allows manufacturers to package their products in clear glass or plastic rather than opaque or dark packaging. It is also used in laundry and household cleaning products.[24a]

Read the label of everything you buy!

The California's State Legislature's Proposition 65 passed in 1986 heralds the beginning of awareness and change in behavior. The law states that all products that contain benzophenone must be labeled with:

"WARNING: This product contains benzophenone, a chemical known to the State of California to cause cancer. The product shall bear clear and reasonable warnings for all products that do not qualify as Compliant Products, in a conspicuous, prominent, easily read and understood way. A warning such as, shall be affixed to the packaging, labeling or directly on each product provided for sale in the California State. This warning is for products with only one cancer-causing chemical, benzophenone. A similar approach is necessary if the products are sold via mail order catalog or internet to customers located in California."[25]

Avobenzone is also included on this list. Therefore, it makes no sense to continue to promote the use of chemicals for preventing cancers that have now finally been recognized as causing cancer, and legislation is passed that the manufacturers must affix a warning label that they have been known to cause cancer.

> Sold to the public as cancer protective, yet needs a warning label that they have been proven to cause cancer.

The Benzophenone HMB

HMB, chemical name (2'-dihydroxy-4-methoxy-benzophenone), is used as a UV stabilizer in cosmetic, pharmaceutical, and plastic products. In 1979, it was identified in 62 different cosmetic products, the largest product lines identified were nail polish and enamel. HMB is used in skin moisturizing products and sunscreen lotions, usually in conjunction with other UV filters.[26]

More details regarding the harm this chemical can cause is described in the **Section: Body Penetration** (later in this chapter).

Cinnamates: OMC and OC

Methoxycinnamate (OMC)

Giving rats octyl methoxycinnamate (OMC) throughout pregnancy and nursing, researchers, after finding that OMC exposure during pregnancy can affect both the reproductive and neurological development of rat offspring, expressed concern that humans are exposed to it from sunscreens and cosmetics. They identified marked decreases in the thyroid hormone, T4; behavioral changes; and decreased sperm counts, testosterone, and prostate weights.[27] More harm from OMC is detailed in the **Section: Body Penetration** (later in this chapter).

Octocrylene (OC)

Octocrylene (OC) is a cinnamate used in sunscreen and daily care cosmetic products. Studies show that it accumulates in aquatic, or plant and animal water organisms, and is toxic, especially to the reproductive system.[28]

Avobenzone

Avobenzone is also known by the trade names Parsol 1789, Milestab 1789, Eusolex 9020, Escalol 517, Neo Heliopan 357 and INCI butyl methoxydibenzoylmethane. This is not a comprehensive list of all the names that can also appear on a product ingredient list. There is no doubt that it absorbs into the skin, as it is found to significantly penetrate through the epidermis of the skin, however it has been included in chemical sunscreen formulas because it has been believed that avobenzone can absorb UVA, while the other EDs do not.[29]

However, 2004 research found that it **DOES NOT PROTECT SKIN CELLS FROM THE UVA RADIATION**. It also increases oxidative effects, and leads to significant cell death, as well as decreases the body's natural protective effects of its antioxidants.[30] The decrease of the body's antioxidants shows that the chemical causes oxidative stress in the cells, which results in damage as it leaves them less able to detoxify or to repair. All these toxic effects makes it no wonder that avobenzone is also included in California's Proposition 65 law that there has to be a warning label on products containing this chemical, stating it has been known to cause cancer.[31]

Camphors

There are several camphors awaiting approval by the U.S. FDA for incorporating them to be used and labeled as a *sunscreen* ingredient in the U.S, whereas they are allowed to be sold for that use in other countries. The FDA currently approves the camphor known under the trade names of Ecamsule, and Mexoryl SX (terephthalylidene dicamphor sulfonic acid) in certain drug formulations.[32]

The U.S. FDA has not allowed the camphors that the European Union has allowed to be included in sunscreen products, but they do allow BP3, which also demonstrates hormonal disruption. Looking at hormonal pathways, both of these ultraviolet filters disrupt regulatory genes of major hormones involved with progesterone and insulin, creating harm in the embryos. Looking at environmental contamination, researchers stated in a 2016 study that: "Further effort is needed to develop environmental risk assessment studies on these pollutants, particularly for aquatic invertebrate model organisms."[33] It is amazing that risk assessment studies were not performed 40 years earlier, before these chemicals were unleashed on the planet, allowing them to contaminate all life.

Even though the U.S. FDA has NOT ALLOWED a camphor to be listed as an ingredient that is *active*, meaning that it is in the formulation as a sunscreen, the FDA DOES ALLOW the camphor 3-benzylidene camphor (3-BC) to be used as a UV light absorber for cosmetic and personal care products. They state that in this case, the ingredient is utilized to protect the product from deterioration by absorbing UV light, and is listed as an *inactive* ingredient. However, a study shows 3-BC creates many of the altered reproductive changes that are created by the 4-MBC camphor the FDA does not allow, plus 3-BC can instigate irregular menstrual cycles.[34] Women are utilizing cosmetics and personal care products with no warning that they can disrupt their hormonal balance and menstrual cycles.

There has been a lot of pressure put on the FDA to allow what has been promoted as the *better, more protective* sunscreen chemicals, that Europe has allowed. Yet, the camphors are what the

European regulators have been allowing to be sold to the public. Even though the U.S. FDA allows harmful sunscreen chemicals to be marketed in the U.S., at least it got it right about the harmful dangers of the camphors of 3-benzylidene camphor (3-BC), and 4-methylbenzylidene camphor (4-MBC).[35] Studies have revealed the fetal and reproductive harms they cause. However, the studies also reveal that ALL the sunscreen chemicals allowed by the FDA are harmful to living tissue, especially the reproductive system, and cause disrupted fetal development.

Many studies are corroborating the identification of chemical UV filters causing changes in hormonal actions, altering estrogen, androgen and progesterone activity, which cause both reproductive and developmental toxicity, and impair functioning of the thyroid, liver, and kidneys. Benzophenones disrupt estrogen and testosterone receptors, and receptors that are within the cell nucleus. Cinnamates disrupt estrogen and thyroid receptors, and also cell nucleus receptors. Camphors disrupt estrogen, testosterone, and progesterone receptors.[36] Blocking the receptors of our major hormones and of the cells themselves reveals why these sunscreen chemicals impact the entire body.

Estrogenic Sunscreen Chemicals

Two sunscreen chemicals, octyl methoxycinnamate (OMC) and 4-methyl-benzylidene camphor (4-MBC), as well as the preservative, butyl paraben, used in sunscreens, all exert estrogenic influences.[37] There has been attention paid to BPA in plastics, because it exerts estrogenic influences, with a lot of legislation proposed and passed to take it out of products, but there has not been the same recognition or call for removal of these estrogenic chemicals from sunscreens, but the harm is the same.

The fact that octyl methoxycinnamate (OMC) has been allowed in sunscreens for decades and methylbenzylidene camphor (4-MBC) allowed to be in cosmetics if it is not listed as a sunscreen, means that the entire American population now has these chemicals floating around in their blood, and being distributed to every organ in the body. They state the "health effects are unknown," which shows that Americans have not been protected by the agencies that were put in place to protect them and that they have trusted to do so. We have been mindlessly using these chemicals without realizing that they were not fully researched before the FDA approved them for use in all sunscreens.

Body Penetration

In the 1980s and 1990s studies were being published that left no doubt the that body absorbs sunscreen chemicals. Rats dosed with HMB (a benzophenone) show that the chemical and metabolites of this chemical appear in the bile ducts within four hours.[38]

In 1992, 26 years ago, a study was published in the *Toxicity Report Series* that identified HMB causes harm to both our liver and kidneys, yet there has been no call to reduce or stop the use of HMB in sunscreens.[39] Many studies have further identified that benzophenone chemical UV filters are easily absorbed by the skin and enter into the blood circulation, allowing them to accumulate in tissues, including the liver, brain, and fat cells.[40] When applying both the mosquito repellent, DEET, along with BP3, the combination of chemicals increases the absorption of both of them through the skin.[41]

Multiple studies confirm substantial absorption and distribution of the chemical filters, BP3, 4-methylbenzylidene camphor (4-MBC) and octyl methoxycinnamate (OMC).[42] They are found in the blood two hours after application to the skin in both human males and females.[43] Other researchers found that BP3 accumulates in the liver, kidney, and testicles.[44]

After skin administration of BP3, it can be detected in the blood of rats within five minutes, with metabolites of BP3 found in all the tissues examined. The liver contains the highest amount followed by the kidney, spleen and testicles, respectively.[45] Even more researchers found that BP3 after being absorbed enters into the systemic circulation, and is transported to different organs, particularly the liver, brain and fat tissue. It accumulates in the blood, liver, and brain after repeated topical applications, creating toxicity to both nerve cells (neurons) and astrocytes (cells in the brain that surround neurons to support and insulate them).[46]

Dosing rats with BP and HMB, scientists found the concentration of BP and HMB showed peak levels in the blood at four hours after administration. Their metabolites, however, decreased much more slowly over time compared to the parent compounds, making the concerned researchers state: "Thus, our results indicate that such metabolites might have more significant adverse effects than the parent compounds over the long term."[47] Not much research has been done on the compounds or metabolites that sunscreen chemicals change into in the body. This identifies that researchers need to also be looking at the biochemical effects of the metabolites of the chemicals, as they change into altered forms, or metabolites, within the body.

When human volunteers applied BP3, OMC, and 4-MBC for two weeks, all three of these sunscreen chemicals were detectable in the volunteers' blood and urine, and their reproductive hormone levels were altered. Observing the amount of these "estrogenic" sunscreen compounds in the blood, the researchers expressed concern for children who had not reached puberty, because they are considered to be more sensitive to low levels of hormone action due to their low levels of reproductive hormones. Also, young children have less developed pathways to eliminate drugs and larger surface area per body weight than adults, which could result in greater absorption and build-up within their bodies. They concluded that sunscreen treatment similar to the treatment given in this study ". . . might have adverse effects in children".[48]

The chemicals also get through to the developing fetus. In analyzing maternal blood along with amniotic fluid, cord blood, and fetal blood: BP1, BP3, 4-methyl-benzophenone (4-MBP), were detectable in amniotic fluid, cord blood, and fetal blood, and 4-hydroxy-benzophenone (4-HBP) is detectable in amniotic fluid and cord blood.[49] There is no doubt that these chemicals disrupt fetal programming. See **Section: Fetal Development.**

It is amazing that a study published in a 2012 *Journal of Andrology*, almost 40 years after sunscreens had been massively promoted as essential to protect from skin cancers states: "Evidently, use of sunscreens is effective in prevention of sunburns in various models. However, evidence for their protective effects against melanoma skin cancer is less conclusive." "Few human studies have investigated potential side effects of UV-filters, although human exposure is high as UV-filters in sunscreens are rapidly absorbed from the skin. One of the UV-filters, BP-3 [benzophenone-3], has been found in 96% of urine samples in the U.S. and several UV-filters in 85% of Swiss breast milk samples. It seems pertinent to evaluate whether exposure to UV-filters contribute to possible adverse effects on the developing organs of [fetuses] and children."[50]

Mothers transfer these toxic chemicals to their children.

In addition to the fact that UV radiation blockers cannot prevent melanoma and skin cancers, every FDA chemical or mineral approved for a SPF (Solar Protective Factor) rating is toxic to the body and all marine life. Their fat solubility (able to combine with or dissolve into fat) allows them to readily cross the blood-brain barrier (BBB), which means they enter the brain. Not much research has been done regarding their ability to be toxic, however, it is known that endocrine disruptors can impair nerve transmission, and produce toxic effects to nerves.[51]

Additive Effect

The standard routine of testing one chemical at a time to determine its individual safety is no longer adequate. Studies must be conducted that look at these chemicals and their effects when mixed together, as sunscreen formulations are to ensure covering the entire UV spectrum.

When researchers exposed protozoa (single-celled microscopic animals) to four sunscreen chemicals: 2-ethylhexyl 4-methoxycinnamate (EHMC), BP3, 4-MBC and OC; they found impaired cell membrane and oxidation injuries, especially from BP3. Since there are multiple chemicals in the sunscreen formulations and they found an additive effect, they concluded that it is imperative to investigate the additive toxic action of multiple sunscreen chemicals being combined, rather than just investigating one chemical at a time.[52]

> Consider everything you place on or in your body as to how it is going to impact its ecosystem.

Chapter 3
Titanium Dioxide (TiO$_2$) and Zinc Oxide (ZnO)

As the public became more educated about sunscreen chemicals, they began avoiding the chemical endocrine disruptive (EDs) formulas. As if the hormonally or ED chemicals are not enough, sunscreen manufacturers are advertising formulations that do not have EDs as "Kid Safe." This a total misrepresentation of the truth. The zinc oxide (ZnO) and titanium dioxides (TiO$_2$) are extremely toxic in their own ways. ZnO and TiO$_2$ block both UVA and UVB. ZnO can block more UVA radiation than TiO$_2$, which blocks more UVB. They are used because the chemical endocrine or hormone disruptors usually block either only UVA or UVB, or only small portions of UVB, so several of them have to be utilized in sunscreen formulations to create a "broad spectrum" of coverage.

The parent material of TiO$_2$ and ZnO are white pastes, which have been *thought to be safe* when used in their bulk (larger) size. (They are not safe, see **Section: Bulk vs. NPs**). That safeness belief is why the FDA allowed them to be marketed without evidence of *no harm* when brought down to such small sizes of nano and micro. The white paste is what we used to see on lifeguards' noses. The pharmaceutical companies that manufacture the sunscreens realized people do not want to look like white ghosts, so they trick the eye to be unable to see them by bringing down their particle size to what has been called nanosize. However, when the size of TiO$_2$ is reduced down to nanoscale (diameter < 100 nanometer), its activity and chemical properties are significantly different from the properties of their bulk size analogue.[53]

There is no doubt that these particles penetrate the body. Just look at the pictures of a human skin cell on the next page. All the dark spots are TiO$_2$ particles that penetrated deeply into the cells, and even penetrated inside the nucleus of the cell, where they are capable of disrupting cell division.

Human Epidermal Cells with Internalized TiO2 Nanoparticles

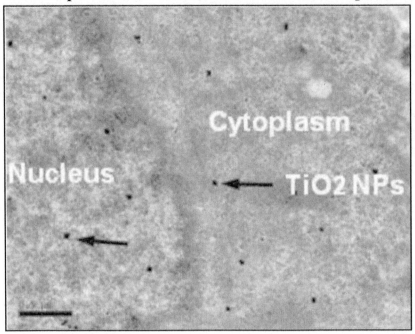

Figure 5.

Source: Shukla RK, Sharma V, Pandey AK, Singh S, Sultana S, Dhawan
A. ROS-mediated genotoxicity induced by titanium dioxide
nanoparticles in human epidermal cells. *Toxicol in Vitro*. 2011.
25(1):231-241. Epub 2010 Nov 17. Reprinted with permission.

Numerous commercial products contain titanium dioxide (TiO2)
and zinc oxide (ZnO) nanoparticles (NPs), however, many of
these are not labelled as containing NPs. The FDA does not require manufacturers to list the size of the TiO2 and ZnO particles
they use for sunscreen manufacturing, so the consumer is not
aware of the potential dangers in the formulations they are buying. It is a tragedy that many of the medical experts and authori-
ties the public has come to trust and to rely on to follow their

guidance are promoting *natural mineral* sunscreens that contain either ZnO or TiO$_2$ as safe. They use the word *safe*, **yet, nothing could be further from the truth.** These cause as much harm as the endocrine disrupting (EDs) chemicals. I saw the harm in the research six years ago, and since then researchers have supplied overwhelming evidence that they are much more harmful than originally determined.

Yet, the use of titanium dioxide nanoparticles (TiO$_2$ NPs) has proliferated in many areas creating massive exposure to us and our environment. They are used as additives for paints, lacquers, papers, and in the foods we eat, even in tooth paste, chewing gum, candy and puddings, so our exposure has skyrocketed over the last two decades since the FDA approved their use in sunscreens in 1999.

The size of a nanometer (nm) is equal to one billionth of a meter, or 0.000000001 of a meter. In sunscreens, the definition of nano is less than 100 nm. Micro is greater than 100 nanometers. These are in the range of approximately 1/5,000th the size of a human hair. A human hair is about 75 microns (75 μm) or 75,000 nm in diameter. Manufacturers are claiming that their formulations are safe because they are micronized size and not nanosized, and saying they are *safe* because they are *natural mineral* preparations.

They claim the larger sizes are not harmful. When you are down at 1/5,000th the diameter of a human hair, the difference between nano at 60 nm and micro at 160 nm is meaningless, and studies prove they both cause cellular damage, yet, advertising heralds them as being safe for kids. However, the research does not back up their claims. More than one study has found the micronized size causes damage similar to nanosize particles. One study that gave mice either the micronized, 160 nm, or the nanosized, 33 nm, found identical damage that included increased cell division in the esophagus and colon cell lining, increased frequency of sperm with two nuclei, and increased cell death in the testicles.

In addition, both sizes caused DNA damage in the cells of bone marrow, the nanosized caused DNA damage to the cells in the liver, while the micronized size caused abnormal cell division in bone marrow cells. The researchers determined that the DNA toxicity was due to inflammation and oxidative stress caused by the NPs, and they concluded that: "Given the increasing use of TiO(2) nanoparticles, these findings indicate a potential health hazard associated with exposure to TiO(2) particles."[54] One study even concluded: " . . . the micrometer particles of TiO(2) caused more DNA damage compared to the nanoparticles, which is likely explained by the crystal structures."[55]

> Non-nano, microsize is not safer and should also be avoided. These are changes in marketing wording to get us to continue purchasing their products, as the science does not support their claims.

Bulk vs. Nano Particles (NPs)
In 2015 when researchers compared TiO_2 NPs to TiO_2 bulk (the parent white paste compound that has been considered safe), they found that both forms created cell membrane damage after 24 hours of exposure. This is important because the belief has been that bulk white paste TiO_2 was safe. Therefore, the FDA did not require testing of the smaller nano or microsize particles. They reasoned that if it was safe in the parent (bulk) compound, it would still be safe in the nanosize particles. However, this study shows that the bulk white paste form is, itself, harmful, and reveals that the tremendous reduction in size makes the nano and micro particles behave extremely differently.[56]

What has not been taken into account is that this micronization changes the properties of these oxides. Due to their tiny size, they can penetrate the skin and other tissues easily, and are more reactive with biological tissues, leading to issues with their safety. When the NPs are exposed to UV radiation, as when people are in the sun, the UV radiation interaction leads to the generation of free radicals, which are highly damaging molecules on the NPs surface with unpaired electrons that cause cellular damage. The amount of damage increases as the size of the oxide decreases. They cause damage to the cells and to the DNA within the cells. The problem is that their size is so small, present technology does not include devices that can measure them easily. Even though there is now sufficient evidence of the damage they are causing to cells and lab animals, studies have difficulty documenting the damage, which leaves many questions unanswered as to their safety and the amount of damage they are capable of creating.[57]

Promoting that a product is *non-nano* or is safe because it is *micronized* is totally misleading to the public. In analyzing the sunscreen powders that are used to formulate sunscreens, it is found they contain **BOTH NANO AND MICRONIZED PARTICLES.** Below is a detailed analysis of the particle sizes of TiO$_2$ and ZnO from the powder that is utilized to create sunscreen products.

Particle Sizes Found In Sunscreen Powders: Used for Sunscreen Formulations[58]

	Reported In Percentages (%) by Nanometer Sizes			
	TiO$_2$		**ZnO**	
Nano	45%	<50 nm	33%	<100 nm
Nano	30%	50-100	28%	100-200
Mirconized	15%	100-150	25%	200-300
Mirconized	8%	150-200	12%	300-400
	2%	>200	2%	>400
Total Nano	**70%**	**<100 nm**	**33%**	**<100 nm**

Table 2.

This analysis identifies that 70% of TiO$_2$ powder is less than 100 nm or nanosized with 30% microsized, while ZnO powder contains 67% microsized, with 33% nanosized. This means that any formulation of sunscreens, whether it claims to be micro or bulk, also contains nanosized particles. There is no technology that can sort these tiny particles to ensure only a certain size is used in any product.

Research has determined that adverse effects of nanoparticles on human health are on an individual basis including genetics, existing conditions, amount of exposure, and the chemistry of the nanoparticle, which includes their size, shape, and the amount that they cluster together. Live studies show that when nanoparticles are inhaled, they are less efficiently removed than larger particles in the lungs. The end result is lung damage, which then allows the nanoparticles to travel through the blood, lymphatic, and nervous systems to all tissues and organs, including the brain. Their toxicity arises from their minute size, which allows them to penetrate cells and the structures within the cells, including the nucleus and DNA, disrupting normal functioning of our cells, and harming DNA.[59]

Photochemical & Photobiological Sciences in 2010 published a paper that claimed the use of nano forms of TiO_2 and ZnO is considered a "negligible risk of no consequence to human health," including the claim that they do not penetrate the skin. With all the evidence of skin penetration and their presence in various organs, along with disruption of biological processes in all species investigated, their claim amounts to the same as a 1947 *Time* magazine advertisement that claimed scientific studies had determined "DDT was safe and a benefactor for all humanity". Yet, 25 years later the extreme harm that DDT causes was recognized, including that it is passed through the placenta into developing fetuses. This identification of the extreme harm it actually causes led to it being banned from use in the U.S.A. in 1972.[60]

The Great Expectations Held for DDT have Been Realized

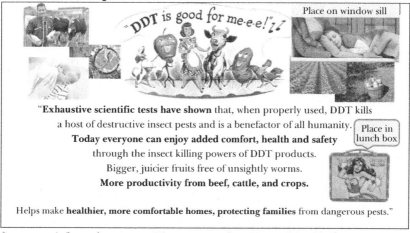

"**Exhaustive scientific tests have shown** that, when properly used, DDT kills a host of destructive insect pests and is a benefactor of all humanity. **Today everyone can enjoy added comfort, health and safety** through the insect killing powers of DDT products. Bigger, juicier fruits free of unsightly worms. **More productivity from beef, cattle, and crops.**

Helps make **healthier, more comfortable homes, protecting families** from dangerous pests."

Source: **Advertisement *Time* magazine June 30, 1947**
[This is a recreation - not the original.]

The acceptance by the public that it was beneficial, and safe, however, has led to DDT and a derivative of it, DDE, being linked to breast cancer and obesity several generations after it was banned. "Thirty-three years after its use was banned in the United States, DDT is still detectable in about 5 to 10% of this country's residents, and DDE is detectable in nearly everyone."[61]

> All sunscreens may become known as the DDT of the 21st century.

Today, there is plenty of proof that reduced sized TiO$_2$ and ZnO should be banned. In a 2014 publication, researchers gave mice TiO$_2$, ZnO and Al$_2$O$_3$ (aluminum oxide – which among other uses is for car exhaust purification) nanoparticles for 21 days. They found the nanoparticles inside the cytoplasm and nucleus of the brain cells of the mice. They identified reactive oxygen species (ROS) indicating significant oxidative stress in red blood cells, liver and brain, and disrupted antioxidant enzyme activities. The rats showed significant increased levels in the neurotransmitters dopamine and norepinephrine in the brain's cerebral cortex, and increased brain oxidative stress, which indicates these nanoparticles are potentially toxic to nerve cells in the brain. In order of toxicity, ZnO was the most toxic, followed by aluminum oxide and titanium dioxide. They concluded that the nanoparticles' major toxicity is through the generation of ROS that leads to oxidative stress.[62]

Nanosized TiO_2 topically applied for 60 days to hairless mice resulted in pathological lesions (injury) in the skin, liver, and brain. The research also shows that application to the skin over a prolonged time results in reduced collagen in the skin, which would create skin aging. The researchers concluded: "Altogether, the present study indicates that nanosize TiO(2) may pose a health risk to humans after dermal (skin) exposure over a relative long time period."[63] This 2009 article proves damage from long-term use (and long-term use is what is being promoted), leads to increased skin aging, which is one of the reasons sunscreen use has been promoted – claiming it decreases skin aging.

Almost all make-up today has TiO_2 NPs, which you can determine by looking at whether it has a Sun Protective Factor (SPF) ranking. Any SPF ranking means that the product contains one or more of the harmful materials described in this book, because the FDA will not allow products that do not contain one of their approved sunscreen chemicals to even be tested for a SPF value ranking.

Differing Forms of TiO_2 – Create Slightly Differing Harms

Rutile and Anastase Explanation
TiO_2 occurs in several forms that are all the same mineral, but they have different structures. The most common natural form of TiO_2 is called rutile, another is called TiO_2 anatase. Studies that look at both these forms of TiO_2 in sunscreens have found that cells take up both forms of the mineral. They also determined the anatase form of the nanoparticles caused strong phototoxicity (meaning it is more toxic when it is exposed to light), which includes decreasing mitochondrial activity (energy producing) reducing the cells' ability to produce energy, damaging cellular membranes, and creating oxidative stress when they are exposed to 4 hours of the very radiation they are supposed to be used to protect from: ultraviolet A (UVA) irradiation.[64]

Contrary to marketing claims that micro is safer, when researchers exposed hamster embryo cells to either nanosized and microsized anatase and rutile TiO_2, they found that the rutile microparticles induced more DNA damage than the nanosized particles. Exposure to anatase nanoparticles and microparticles produced similar levels of DNA damage.[65] The European Union reviewing the safety of products sold in Europe stated that one of the products they were testing was a yield from regular production of TiO_2 and determined that it was 95% rutile form, with about 5% anatase.[66] So, both forms are in sunscreen formulations. This puts to rest that microsized particles are safer than nanosized in the marketing of these products. They are not safer, they are all harmful.

Zinc Oxide (ZnO)
There is no doubt these small metals are absorbed. Humans with healthy skin exposed to sunscreen products containing ZnO NPs for 5 days leads to zinc ions in their blood and urine, levels that continued to increase even after stopping their use. This same research identified that women absorbed more than the men.[67]

Other researchers have found that there is more absorption through skin that is damaged, whether it is from sunburn or physical damage, and they remain in wounded skin.[68] Still other researchers have found that there is more penetration when NPs are exposed to ultraviolet light, which is why people use sunscreens, they are going out into the sun's ultraviolet light.[69]

Again, they have been brought to market without proper testing as to their possibility of harm. **In 2013**, a study stated: "Although zinc oxide nanoparticles (ZnO-NP) are being used on a wide scale in the world consumer market, **their potential hazards on humans remain largely unknown.**"[70] This is almost 15 years after FDA approved their use for sunscreens.

And what about making sure that they would cause no harm to a baby's development? In a 2013 study published in *The Journal of Toxicological Sciences*, the researchers stated that the health effects of ZnO NPs during pregnancy on the offspring are largely unknown. How can sunscreen use be pushed so hard on the public when the health effects and effects of exposure to ZnO during pregnancy on offspring are largely unknown?[71]

There is plenty of evidence now that they are toxic to reproduction and fetal growth. **See Section on: Reproduction.** All these factors are important to keep in mind. Since ZnO NPs cross into babies in the womb, women should never be exposed to ZnO.

Aluminum

Researchers testing sunscreens for the presence of aluminum found aluminum in all seven products they tested, whether it was listed on the label or not. Since it is an oxidizer, it increases the oxidation damage in the skin.[71a]

Aluminum is used in processing nanoparticles.[71b]

This is an additional concern regarding sunscreen use, as "Aluminum is related with many brain diseases including Alzheimer's disease, Parkinson's disease, and multiple sclerosis."[71c]

Summary of Neurotoxicity of Aluminum

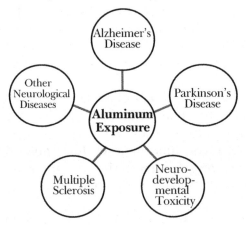

Figure 6.

Source: Inan-Eroglu E, Ayaz A. Is aluminum exposure a risk factor for neurological disorders? *J Red Med Sci.* 2018; 23:51. Reprinted with permission.

Spray Sunscreens – *Do Not Breathe Them In*
Many manufacturers make sunscreen chemicals available in spray bottles, which results in spraying everyone at the beach or at the pool. This promoted convenience actually makes them more harmful as they become airborne and are inhaled. Inhalation is associated with increased exposure of the ZnO NPs in the brain, because the olfactory nerves can directly transport the particles into the brain. Researchers do find ZnO NPs in rats' brains following nasal administration.[72]

The same is true for TiO$_2$. Researchers found TiO$_2$ NPs created oxidation damage in the lungs and blood, as well as in lymph nodes, liver, kidney, and spleen. They also identified that the TiO$_2$ NPs appeared to be partly transferred to olfactory bulbs and to the brain.[73] It is recommended to not use any sprays and to stay away from anyone spraying it on themselves or their children, as it is carried by the wind and can contaminate everyone in the area.

We recommend removing your children from the area when sunscreens are being sprayed. It is too easy for the chemicals to enter the brain through the nose.

Chapter 4
Reproduction:
Detrimental For Both Expectant Mothers and Their Fetuses

Many researchers have published studies that identify sunscreen chemicals alter and interfere with reproduction. As long ago as 1992, a National Toxicology Program report by Dr. J. French was published that identified body-wide toxicity and reproductive harm from sunscreen chemicals. Exposing rats and mice to either topical or oral HMB (2-hydroxy-4-methoxybenzophenone) created similar effects. The alterations included decreases in sperm, lengthened menstrual cycle, increased liver and kidney weights; microscopic changes in the kidneys, comprising tubular dilatation with white blood cell protein casts (indicator of kidney inflammation). Damaging alterations to the liver included dilatation, tubular regeneration, papillary degeneration, and inflammation identified in liver lesions that occurred in both rats and mice.[74] The National Toxicology Program 2018 Website includes this article by J.E. French.[75] This shows that the government has known about the body-wide damage this sunscreen chemical causes, and yet it has not been banned from being used in sunscreens.

Many researchers investigating the camphors 4-MBC and 3-BC have found decreased weight in pregnant female rats, delayed male puberty, increased reproductive organ weights in adult males and females, enhanced prostate growth, impaired female sexual behavior, altered development in the hypothalamo-pituitary-gonadal system, estrogen-regulated gene expression in the reproductive organs, and alterations in the brain regions connected with reproductive organ control and sexual behavior. With also finding there is a bioaccumulation or buildup in both wild life and humans, the researchers urge a comprehensive analyses of the toxic potential of sunscreen chemicals, especially in regards to reproduction and development in offspring.[76]

A 2012 review identified the potential adverse effects sunscreens induce in experimental animals including toxicity to reproduction, developmental toxicity, and disruption of thyroid function due to disturbance of the organs involved, and the hypothalamic-pituitary-thyroid axis (HPT). The researchers as well as other researcher state these hormonally active compounds are in young children, and that they are in our water and wastewater urging that we need to develop a system to remove these from our water systems.[77]

An article published in 2013 identified that female rats exposed to ZnO nanoparticles for two weeks before mating and through 4 days after delivery resulted in a reduced number of born or live pups, decreased body weights of pups, and increased fetal resorption (disintegration and absorption of the fetus back into the uterus). Upon finding ZnO NPs in breast tissue of the female rats, and in the liver and kidneys of the offspring, which identifies developmental toxicity in the offspring, the researchers concluded: "These results indicate that zinc oxide nanoparticles-exposure before and during pregnancy and lactation (nursing) could pose health risks to pregnant women and their fetus."[78]

In a 2015 article, researchers theorized that it is TiO_2 inducing oxidative stress in the testicles that creates disrupted sperm generation. They found mice exposed to TiO_2 NP developed lesions in the testicles and epididymis (tubules sperm pass through), reduced numbers of sperm, reduced sperm motility, and increased numbers of abnormal sperm.[79]

A study published in 2017 exposing hens and their embryos to ZnO NPs found that ZnO nanoparticles are toxic to both the ovaries and the embryos, finding decreased cell growth or increased cell death in embryos. They also identified damage in DNA replication and repair ability in cells in the ovaries that could develop into embryos. They concluded: "Our investigation, along with others, suggests that ZnO NPs are toxic to female reproductive systems [ovaries (oocytes-immature egg cells)] and are subsequently embryo-toxic. Precautions should therefore be taken in situations of human exposure."[80]

Eight studies of TiO2 NPs on mice and rats all show reproductive harm.[81] The damage these studies identified includes:

Premature egg development
Death of cells in the ovary
Deformed follicle growth
Inhibited oocyte (immature egg) maturation
DNA toxicity
Cell toxicity
Cross placenta-affecting fetal CNS development
Neurotoxic to neonatal and adult brains
Accumulates in placenta
Placenta toxicity

Researchers are proving TiO2 NPs toxicity to the male reproductive tract (testicles, prostate, and epididymis). They are so small they can cross the blood-testis barrier, accumulating in testicles resulting in testicular lesions, sperm malformations, and alterations in sex hormone levels. They also have found that over 140 genes are either increased or decreased in their actions. Based on their findings, the researchers warned that the production of TiO2 should be carried out with caution and that humans of reproductive age should be cautious in the use of TiO2.[82]

Many researchers are finding similar results. Mice receiving TiO2 nanoparticles for 35 days developed testicular changes including:

Cellular changes in testicular tissue
Increased cell death
Decreased testicular weight
Decreased testosterone levels
Reduced sperm quality

The administration of quercetin, a potent flavonoid antioxidant, effectively improved all of the above, which continues to demonstrate that TiO2 NPs create oxidation damage.[83]

Females – Beware of Food Products and Cosmetics that Contain TiO2 Nanoparticles

Since the TiO2 NPs do not leave the body, females should guard against ever using products that contain TiO2 or other products that contain potentially nanosized materials, such as ZnO NPs. The U.S. FDA has approved titanium dioxide (TiO2) materials that includes nanosized TiO2 (n TiO2) to be used as food additives, especially in white foods as TiO2 helps to make products like puddings white. Scientists citing that TiO2 has toxic effects on the gastrointestinal tract and other tissues, determined to find the sources and concentrations that are in popular foods. They found TiO2 particles in white-colored seafoods and fish products. They warned that: "Together, these results show relatively high concentrations of TiO2 particles in some seafood and surimi [fish paste] products available in the market, and our findings therefore call for attention on TiO2 particle exposure and uptake through daily foods."[84]

Fetal Development

Now that there are no doubts that sunscreen chemicals are absorbed into the body, it is imperative to determine if they can be transferred to the fetus and if they are capable of interfering with the normal development of our children. The placenta has specialized cells to prevent toxins from entering the fetus while it is developing. Research has identified that EDs and nanoparticles can cross the placental barrier. BP3 being incorporated into our bodies is creating multi-generational health consequences. In looking at levels of BP3 in maternal urinary samples, more BP3 in the pregnant mother's urine correlated with increased overall weight and head circumference of male babies. The researchers stated that these outcomes should raise concerns about developmental toxicity of UV filters.[85]

The public has acquired a lot of information that has resulted in making them stay away from sunscreen chemicals that are primarily hormone mimics or endocrine disruptors, however, the research shows that the TiO2 and ZnO NPs can be just as detrimental. Researchers investigated the possibility of the effects by exposing pregnant mice to ZnO NPs. On examining the brains of their pups, they found that the turnover levels of the neurotransmitter, dopamine, was increased in major parts of the brain, including the prefrontal cortex, neostriatum, nucleus accumbens, and amygdala. An increased turnover of serotonin was also found throughout the brain, except for the cerebellum.[86]

All these alterations of chemicals within the brain cannot help but lead to alterations in behavior. Children diagnosed on the autism spectrum show dysfunction in the prefrontal cortex, one of the areas of the brain that shows changes in neurotransmitter levels on maternal exposure to TiO_2.[87]

After treating pregnant rats with TiO_2 NPs, researchers examined the 1-day-old pups, finding TiO_2 NPs concentrated in their brains' hippocampus. Later testing of the pups as they aged revealed they had significant impairment in learning and memory, critical functions that the hippocampus performs.[88]

Other researchers identified pregnant mice treated with TiO_2 results in alteration to the cerebral cortex, and olfactory bulb of the offspring.[89] The alterations to the cerebral cortex identifies that TiO_2 exposure should be examined for autism development, as autistic brains show abnormal cellular arrangements in their cerebral cortex.[90]

Research has also identified in pregnant mice treated with TiO_2 NPs that the gene expression of the nerve cells involved in the neurotransmitter dopamine system are altered. The changes that are seen include increased levels of dopamine and its metabolites in some regions of the fetal brain.[91] These studies identify that maternal exposure to TiO_2 could impair brain and central nervous system development of their offspring that shows up as impaired anti-oxidation within the brain, and alteration of neurotransmitters, which can result in altered neurobehavioral performance, and in psychiatric diseases.[92]

Other researchers found similar results when they exposed pregnant mice to TiO_2. Maternal exposure measured at gestational (pregnancy) days 6, 9, 12, and 15 revealed changes in the offspring gene expression related to brain development, cell death, response to oxidative stress, mitochondria in the brain, inflammation, and neurotransmitters. This study identifies the pregnant mothers pass the TiO_2 on to their offspring creating considerable difficulties in both development and the offsprings' ability for normal functioning. Maternal exposure of mice to TiO_2 nanoparticles may also affect the expression of genes related to the development and function of the central nervous system.[93]

The evidence keeps piling up. Pregnant rats exposed to TiO_2 NPs daily from gestational day (GD) 2 to GD 21, and housed until postnatal day 60 showed significantly reduced cell proliferation in the hippocampus (memory) of the offspring, and in tests they showed significantly impaired learning and memory, identifying TiO_2 NPs have neurotoxic effects on neonatal and adult brains.[94]

The body has the ability to counter the oxidation reactions that occur continually throughout the whole body. This is essential for preventing inflammation in the tissues, which can disrupt their normal functioning. Multiple studies show that TiO_2 disrupts the ability of the body to perform its continual monitoring and repairing of DNA that is essential to maintain good health.

When pregnant mice are exposed to TiO_2 NPs they are found in the placenta, fetal liver and fetal brain. Mice treated with TiO_2 NPs have smaller uteri and smaller fetuses.[95] Pregnant mice exposed to TiO_2 NPs show that TiO_2 NPs significantly impair the growth and development of the placenta and induce fetal death and deformities. The investigators recommend that the use of products that contain TiO_2 NPs should be stopped during pregnancy.[96]

Maternal exposure to anatase TiO_2 nanoparticles results in alterations in 1,887 genes within the first 21 days of development. The genes that are altered are associated with brain development, cell death, response to oxidative stress, brain mitochondria, inflammation, and neurotransmitters. The researchers state their results suggest that maternal exposure to nanoparticles can alter gene expression in the neonatal period and might cause the onset of psychiatric disorders even in adulthood.[97] This is based on the theory of "early developmental origins of adult disease".[98]

If 1,887 genes were altered in the 21 days they studied them, it can be assumed if they studied them for a longer period of time, the number of alterations would continue to mount. Changes in our genes are extremely detrimental to our continued existence, because they control every aspect of our bodies, including our ability to reproduce.

The gene expressions are involved in many of the problems we are seeing today. There are too many to list here, but they include autism, anxiety disorders, Alzheimer's, ADHD, blood brain barrier alterations, epilepsy, mitochondrial disease, Parkinson's, and schizophrenia.[99] With this many alterations, and the difficulty of removing NPs from the body, it would be best if females were never exposed to NPs by making sure that no products they use have a SPF rating, particularly if they plan to become pregnant.

> It is time to acknowledge the true long-term consequences of sunscreen chemicals on our bodies and in our food.

Chapter 5
Hormonal Disruptions:
Creating Gender Bending or Gender Dysphoria
(How Our Children Are Being Impacted)

EDs act on hormone receptors in the nucleus of cells, and on cell membranes, altering hormonal and non-hormonal pathways and their metabolism. If a cell's receptor is blocked by an *imposter*, the proper hormone cannot attach to the cell to perform its essential function. Since EDs are fat soluble, they are easily deposited in tissues; creating prolonged accumulation and release, even when there is no more exposure to the chemicals. They easily cross the placenta, and benzophenones (BPs) have been found in placenta tissue, getting through to developing fetuses, disrupting fetal development of the formation of the reproductive system and key stages of its maturation and its regulatory mechanisms.[100]

Research studies identify that reproductive toxicity arises from cinnamates (OMC), camphors (4-MBC), and a preservative utilized in the sunscreen formulation (PP-propyl paraben), which all show estrogenic activity in fish. They make male fish show estrogenic markers, and since the fish become neither male or female, the researchers call them *intersex* fish.[101] A benzophenone metabolite, BP2, exerts strong estrogenic effects on the uterus, vagina, pituitary, and liver. BP2 also significantly reduces T4 and T3 thyroid hormone levels.[102]

In 2004, researchers published their results regarding common ingredients of personal care products of exposing Zebrafish to polycyclic musk fragrances and to sunscreen chemicals. They found estrogenic effects from BP3, 3-BC, homosalate (HMS), and the camphor 4-MBC. They also found the chemicals work against testosterone receptors and progesterone receptors. "The activity of anti-progestagenic at low concentrations indicates the need to undertake more research to find out about the potential endocrine disrupting effects of these compounds in vivo [in living tissue]."[103]   Anti-progestagenic actions impair progesterone's ability to perform all of its necessary functions, which includes balancing estrogen and being anti-cancer protective.

Looking at trout and human liver cells, BP and all the various forms it changes into within the body – BP1, BP2, BP3 – show strong anti-testosterone effects and also have strong estrogen effects, which act the opposite of our natural human estrogen. The investigators concluded their results: "Overall, the observed anti-androgenic [anti-testosterone] potencies of BP derivatives, . . . support further investigation of their role as endocrine disrupters in humans and wildlife."[104]

Benzophenone 4 has been shown to increase the number of receptors for estrogenic-related genes in male brains, increasing their estrogenic response. BP4 interferes with the expression of genes involved in hormonal pathways and their formation. It expresses estrogenic activity in both the embryo and the adult brain, showing that BP4 interferes with the functioning of the sex hormone system of fish.[105] Research on the camphor 4-MBC or enzacamene, which has been allowed in Europe, has identified that both prenatal and postnatal exposure interferes with male sexual development.[106] Other studies reveal the same harm. It is known that testosterone secreted by fetal testicles plays a key role in the permanent organization of the developing central nervous system toward masculine patterns.[107]

In the National Health and Nutrition Examination Survey (NHANES) 2011-2012 looking at children and adolescents ages 6-19 years, researchers found that both bisphenol A (BPA) found in plastics, and benzophenone-3 (BP3) found in sunscreens significantly reduce total testosterone levels in males. They also identified that females had significantly higher testosterone levels from BPA. They stated that: "These findings are of interest due to the pervasiveness of these chemicals in our environment and the potential impact that altered reproductive hormones, such as testosterone, can have on the development and overall health of children and adolescents." They urged the need for future studies.[108]

This means that males exposed to these chemicals during their fetal development (pregnancy) are subject to disruption of the development of normal masculine character traits. For this to happen, the fetal male brain needs to be bathed in testosterone. Many young people today are stating they are confused as to their sexual orientation. It is no wonder, they have been exposed to so many strong estrogenic and anti-testosterone chemicals that their natural sexual patterning is disrupted throughout their fetal development, with exposure continuing throughout their lives. The use of these anti-testosterone sunscreen chemicals for the last 40 years, combined with the estrogenic exposure from plastics, foods, and meats could be why males and females in greater numbers are experiencing gender identity confusion. There were articles that revealed the hormone disruption, but attention was not brought to them.

How could we disregard scientific articles that revealed such hormone disruption – why was there no attention brought to them? By ignoring them, we have created whole generations that do not feel comfortable living as being female or male.

Chapter 6
How Sunscreens Are Detrimental to Our Health

In 2008, researchers realized there had not been enough information regarding the effects of BPs, since ". . . benzophenone (BP)-type UV filters have become widely used as UV stabilizers in skin-moisturizing products and sunscreen lotions."[109] However, today, there is enough evidence that sunscreen chemicals impact the entire body.

They Generate Reactive Oxygen Species – ROS

Solar ultraviolet radiation (UVR) creates increases in ROS (reactive oxygen species), which are potent oxidizers. The oxidation alters proteins and fats (lipids), produces inflammation, suppresses the immune system, damages DNA, alters the ability for DNA to function, along with alterations to cell cycle, cell proliferation, and cell death. These promote the development of cancer. The changes can also lead to aging effects created by the UV radiation. Since these aging effects are caused by oxidation, researchers have determined that natural anti-oxidants found in plants are capable of reducing the UV induced aging of the skin.[110]

> The oxidation from sunscreens leads to accelerating the aging process – the opposite of what we have been sold.

Sunscreens have been advocated as protection from the sun's harm, yet zinc oxide nanoparticles (ZnO NPs), one of the major sunscreen chemicals, cause the same harm as UV radiation. ZnO NPs main mode of toxicity is that they create oxidative stress by creating reactive oxygen species (ROS).[111]

The inside of the entire body becomes oxidized just as all the rusted oxidation on the outside of this truck!

The sunscreen chemicals cause the same type of harm the public has been warned about that UV radiation causes, so how can they prevent damage?

Inflammation

ZnO NPs create oxidation and inflammatory effects in the blood and brains of mice dosed with ZnO NPs. When researchers exposed younger adult and older adult mice to ZnO NPs, they found an inflammatory response in the blood and in the brain, increased oxidative stress levels, impaired learning and memory abilities, and pathological changes in the hippocampus, especially in old mice. This indicates there are variable responses to sunscreen exposure and that older individuals are more susceptible to the toxicity to nerve cells that ZnO NPs create. The damage to the hippocampus is especially important as it regulates emotions and consolidates our short-term memory to long-term memory.[112] Difficulty with memory is being expressed by a growing proportion of the population today.

> Inflammation results from the body sending oxygen and white blood cell rich blood to an area where there are "foreign substances," injury, or infection to protect and heal the area.

Heart, Liver, and Immune Function

Rats given ZnO NPs demonstrate significant cardiotoxic effects. A study found that either α-lipoic acid or vitamin E (both antioxidants) prevented the cardiac tissue injury, proving the sunscreen causes oxidation damage throughout the body.[113]

Researchers exposing rat cardiomyocytes (heart cells) to TiO_2 nanoparticles found they acutely alter cardiac excitability and create arrhythmic (irregular heart beat) events.[114] Today, even young people are experiencing heart palpitations, and standard screening tests are not finding the source. Since TiO_2 is in so many products, including makeup, young girls (especially those who are experiencing heart palpitations) in particular should look at all the products they are using on their bodies to see if they contain TiO_2.

Zinc oxide nanoparticles have been identified as toxic to cells in laboratory studies and they cause harm, including death of cells in living animal studies. These researchers found that ZnO NPs are toxic to our important immune cells. Their death leads to increased levels of reactive oxygen species (ROS). The researchers concluded: "Our findings suggest that exposure to ZnO NPs has the potential to impact host immunity."[115]

The conclusions of researchers in a 2016 review of the published studies regarding the actions of ZnO include: "Together these studies suggest that the ZnO NPs contribute to rigidity of the blood vessels and plaque formation, thereby aiding in diseases like atherosclerosis and other cardiovascular diseases." . . . "ZnO NPs reaching the liver interfere with the normal physiology of the cells." . . . "Immune cells encounter the nanoparticle reaching cell system so the toxicity risk is higher for these cells. Sensitized immune cells give way to unwanted inflammatory responses in the body, which in turn can affect normal functioning of other organs. The toxic responses may include inflammation or immune suppression, which in either case can affect the normal physiology."[116]

Depressed immune systems are rampant in society today. Many suffer from frequent infections, or are disabled by mold exposure, or Lyme disease symptoms.

Thyroid Disruption

Dosing rats with BP2 for 5 days to determine the amount of hormone disruption it creates, researchers found it acted like 17beta-estradiol (E2) (women's premenopausal estrogen that exerts the strongest estrogenic effects) on the uterus, liver, vagina and pituitary. It also significantly reduced the thyroid hormones T4 and T3.[117]

Other researchers have had the same decrease in thyroid hormones. Octyl-methoxycinnamate (OMC) is recently classified as an *endocrine active chemical* with estrogenic actions. It interferes with the hypothalamo-pituitary-thyroid (HPT) axis. When rats are treated for 5 days with different doses of OMC or 17beta-estradiol (E2) as a control, E2 did not affect the thyroid hormones, thyroid stimulating hormone (TSH), T4, or T3. OMC, however, caused a decrease in all of these primary thyroid hormones: TSH, T4, and T3.[118]

Rats exposed to OMC show a large reduction in the thyroid hormone T4 in the pregnant females. The male offspring show decreased weights of the prostate and the testicles, and decreased testosterone levels.[119] Many today are being diagnosed with thyroid disorders.

The hormones produced by the thyroid are master hormones that make it possible for all the other hormones to work together in harmony. When the thyroid hormones are not functioning at optimum levels, the body does not operate efficiently, as the body's ecosystem is out of balance. This is a very important function for the body to maintain. These studies clearly identify sunscreen chemicals contribute to the cause by disrupting the thyroid balance in the body, which impacts the ability for the body to function optimally.

Cancers

Breast Cancer
Of six common sunscreen chemicals, five of them show significant estrogenic effects as they increase rates of growth in human breast cancer cells (MCF-7 cells) in a laboratory setting. The chemicals tested are from the families of benzophenones (e.g., BP3), and cinnamates (e.g., OMC), which are allowed by the FDA to be sold in America, and a camphor (4-MBC) that the European Union allows. Rounding out the list are homosalate (HMS) and octyl-dimethyl-PABA (OD-PABA). PABA was one of the original sunscreen chemicals.[120] However, due to a high percentage of allergic reactions to PABA, it has not been incorporated as frequently in more recent formulations.

The vast majority of human breast cancers are estrogen receptor-positive and estrogen-dependent. This means their development and growth can be influenced and driven by environmental estrogen-like endocrine disrupters, such as the sunscreen chemicals. Researchers who are looking into this connection, identify concern over the widespread use of estrogenic mimics like sunscreen chemicals.[121]

The EDs activate breast cancer cells, making them more toxic. In a 2018 study in the *Journal of Applied Toxicology*, six common UV filters used in sunscreens and personal care products were exposed to breast cancer cell lines in the laboratory. They were the benzophenones, BP1, BP2, BP3; the cinnamate, octylmethoxycinnamate (OMC); the camphor, 4-methylbenzilidenecamphor (4-MBC); and homosalate. The researchers conducted the study because these chemicals are found in human milk, and as they are estrogenic, they have a potential to influence breast cancer development. Since the spread of metastatic tumor cells is the main cause of death from breast cancer, they also looked at these chemicals' ability to influence migration and invasion by human breast cancer cell lines. After finding increased motility (the ability to move around), they concluded that exposure to any of these six compounds can increase metastatic migration (spread) and invasion of human breast cancer cells.[122]

These findings show that sunscreen chemicals are capable of contributing to the development of breast cancers, and of creating more deadly metastasizing breast cancer. All the money and effort to cure breast cancer, yet there are advertisements and continual messages everywhere to use sunscreens every time you are in the sun, chemicals that promote the growth of breast cancer cells and their metastatic migration. Stopping use of chemicals that promote the growth and spread of breast cancer cells would be a great place to start prevention.

Prostate Cancer

Studies have identified that endocrine-disrupting compounds can influence both the development and progression of prostate cancer. The estrogenic mimics (imposters) increase the prostate's sensitivity to ED compounds, including sunscreen chemicals, PCBs, and cadmium (cadmium is emanating from computers). The research has also identified that fetal exposure, as well as exposure during puberty, heightens the prostate's sensitivity, leaving today's infants and children at increased risk of prostate cancers as they age.[123]

More Solar Radiation = Less Multiple Myeloma
(How Can that Be?)

In 175 countries, multiple myeloma (cancer of white blood cells) incidence rates are greater at higher latitudes, which means less solar radiation. High UVB radiation and higher blood vitamin D values are associated with lower multiple myeloma incidence rates.[124] The researchers state that the role of vitamin D3 should be investigated for an involvement in reducing the risk of multiple myeloma.

Sun/Solar radiation is good for the body – in moderation.

Leaky Gut and Disrupted Microbiome

Inhaled ZnO NPs, which happens from sunscreen sprays, have been determined to disrupt the normal bacterial flora in the gut, and they create permeability in the lining that can lead to leaky gut.[125] This is a huge factor in the harm created by these particles, and causes concern for the promotion of all the spray sunscreens that are on the market today. We are encouraged to put on sunscreens, especially on our children, however, many people are suffering from the leaky gut conditions, especially those who are diagnosed on the autism spectrum. Today, encouraging use of ZnO sprays claiming they are "Kid Safe" is unacceptable for society's health.

Mitochondrial Dysfunction
Our mitochondria are our energy generators creating about 90% of the chemical energy our cells need to survive. Over the last several decades there has been a tremendous increase in diseases that exhibit mitochondrial dysfunction. Mitochondrial dysfunction results when the cells are no longer able to produce the sufficient quantities of energy that is necessary to keep the body functioning optimally. Decreased energy in the body makes it more difficult for the body to remain healthy. Energy is created within the mitochondrial membrane. ZnO alters the ability for the mitochondrial membrane to function properly to be able to create the energy.[126] ZnO NPs trigger the mitochondrial dysfunction through disrupting the cells' calcium balance (homeostasis), which increases production of reactive oxygen species (ROS), and results in cell death.[127]

Astrocytes are brain cells that can become cancerous. When they are exposed to ZnO NPs, they show mitochondrial dysfunction and cell death. The researchers expressed their results show the need to look at the role ZnO NPs play in the development of neurodegenerative diseases that are proliferating today, many of which demonstrate mitochondrial dysfunction.[128]

So many diseases that have been steadily increasing are identified as having mitochondrial dysfunction. They include neurodegenerative diseases such as amyotrophic lateral sclerosis (ALS), and cardiovascular diseases; atherosclerosis and other heart and vascular conditions; diabetes and metabolic syndrome; autoimmune diseases, such as multiple sclerosis, systemic lupus, and type 1 diabetes; neurobehavioral and psychiatric diseases, such as schizophrenia, and bipolar and mood disorders; gastrointestinal disorders; fatiguing illnesses, such as Gulf War illnesses; musculoskeletal diseases, like fibromyalgia and skeletal muscle hypertrophy/atrophy; and chronic infections.[128a]

Mitochondrial Dysfunction Diseases

- Autism, autism-like features
- Heart, liver or kidney diseases
- Diabetes
- Cancer
- Alzheimer's disease, Parkinson's disease
- Bipolar disorder, Schizophrenia, Anxiety disorders
- Aging
- Cardiovascular disease
- Chronic fatigue syndrome
- Poor growth
- Muscle loss, weakness, pain, low muscle tone, exercise intolerance
- Huntington's disease - jerky movements
- Vision and/or hearing problems
- Learning disabilities, delays in development, mental retardation

Healthy mitochondria are absolutely necessary to keep the body functioning at optimal levels. We should do everything possible to protect their integrity. Considering the vast quantities of sunscreens being sold around the world and so many people utilizing them, as well as polluting our water, it behooves society to look at the sunscreen chemicals contribution in creating this increasing disease phenomenon.

Diabetes

Looking at 51 regions world-wide, LOWER amounts of UVB radiation corresponded with HIGHER incidence rates of type 1 childhood diabetes. Additional confirmation of this connection: incidence rates of type 1 diabetes approach zero in regions world-wide with higher amounts of UVB radiation, with the researchers stating that these results support the role of vitamin D3 in reducing the risk of the disease.[129] This means that those who live in lower latitudes and closer to the equator are exposed to more sunlight, allowing their body to make more vitamin D3, have less incidence of diabetes. Sunscreens by blocking the ability to manufacture vitamin D3, impair the body's ability to protect itself.

ZnO NPs can alter blood sugar. Researchers found that liver cells exposed to ZnO results in an increase of up to 430% in glycogen metabolism, resulting in increased glucose metabolism as well as its release.[130]

When TiO_2 particles enter the bloodstream, white blood cells engulf them and cause an inflammatory response. Researchers microscopically looked at the pancreas of those diagnosed with type 2 diabetes compared with those who are nondiabetic. In the type 2 diabetes, the pancreas was full of TiO_2 particles with an average diameter of 40 nm to 180 nm, with none found in the nondiabetic pancreas. The number of crystals counted as high as 10^8-10^9, or 100 million to 1 billion per gram of diabetic pancreas tissue.[131] Crystals in these numbers must interfere with the normal functions pancreas cells need to perform, so that the body can maintain safe blood sugar levels. This provides even more evidence that claiming a formulation as non-nano and therefore safe is not true as many of the crystal sizes found in the study were well into the micronized size of being greater than 100 nm.

Many today are having blood sugar problems and are being diagnosed as prediabetic or as diabetic. The NPs could be one reason for the increase in out of control blood sugar levels the vast numbers of the population are experiencing today.

NPs Breach the Body's Built-in Protective Barriers

Blood-brain Barrier (BBB) Compromised
Earlier this book provided evidence that the protective barrier of
the placenta is breached by sunscreen chemicals. They also pass
through the blood-brain barrier (BBB), the function of which is
to keep toxic materials from entering our delicate brain. Mice
treated with TiO_2 nanoparticles show lung damage, and changes
in the permeability of the blood-air capillary barrier allowing ac-
cess to the blood circulation reaching tissues outside the lungs,
resulting in injury to the liver and kidneys. The researchers
stated that: "Our results also indicated that TiO_2 NPs might pass
through the blood-brain barrier (BBB), and induce the brain injury through oxidative stress response."[132]

This ability of NPs having the capability to cross the BBB is
confirmed by other researchers.[133] Researchers exposing rats
to TiO_2 NPs found alterations in the permeability of the blood-
brain-barrier (BBB) and brain inflammation, an inflammation
response that increased in aging animals.[134] Again, this identifies
that older people will be at more risk using TiO_2 NPs products.

Multiple studies have found TiO_2 NPs inside the brain, with accumulation within critical parts of the brain, including the hippocampus, the olfactory bulb (odor processing structure), cerebellum, and cerebral cortex. Since the hippocampus is our primary
area of memory and learning this could result in inducing the
neurodegenerative diseases many are experiencing today, such
as Alzheimer's diseases.[135] This identification that TiO_2 is found
in the part of the brain that processes odor makes an even stronger connection of TiO_2 to Alzheimer's as recent research is con-
necting loss of the sense of smell as an early sign that a person
may likely develop Alzheimer's disease.[136]

Brain
One of the ways that nerve cells function is through a balance of
sodium and potassium inside and outside the cell. Exposing the
brain's hippocampus pyramidal cells (which stores and retrieves
memories) to ZnO NPs reveals that the NPs upset nerve cells'

balance of sodium and potassium (homeostasis), and disturbs the physiological functioning of these brain's neurons.[137] Other studies have shown that various NPs can enter the brain across the BBB. Investigations show NPs cause brain tissue damage, to the cells, and to DNA, creating oxidative stress and inflammation that researchers theorize would lead to the onset and progression of neurodegeneration within the brain.[138]

Could the continued absorption of ZnO NPs be partly responsible for the increasing numbers of our elderly losing their memory abilities, and being diagnosed with dementia or Alzheimer's? Considering the rise in the incidence of Alzheimer's disease, the decades of exposure to ZnO should be considered as one of the possible eco-toxic reasons for the ever-increasing numbers of our aging population suffering with these conditions.

Neurotoxicity to the Central Nervous System (CNS)
Researchers have found that TiO_2 NPs are potent inhibitors of cell proliferation in the human central nervous system (CNS) cells after prolonged exposure (up to 10 days). The human cells demonstrate neurotoxic effects after acute doses, and also after prolonged exposure at low doses of TiO_2 nanoparticles.[139] This low dose prolonged exposure is what is happening with sunscreen use, as everyone is encouraged to reapply it every two hours, and after swimming, for maximum benefit. Other researchers reported that TiO_2 NPs create oxidative stress that induces neurotoxicity that is identified in the rats that were exposed to them.[140]

Mental Health
When researchers exposed pregnant mice to ZnO NPs, the ZnO NPs were found throughout the brains of their newborn pups, along with changes in the neurotransmitter, dopamine, they concluded with this much disruption to the major neurotransmitters of the pups' brains from their mothers' exposure to ZnO NPs suggests: "The present study indicated that prenatal exposure to ZnO NPs might disrupt the monoaminergic [i.e., serotonin, dopamine, norepinephrine, epinephrine] system, and suggested the possibility of detrimental effects on the mental health of offspring."[141]

Researchers that exposed pregnant mice to TiO_2 NPs identified: "The results showed that prenatal exposure to TiO_2 NPs impaired the antioxidant status, caused a significant oxidative damage to nucleic acids and lipids in the brain of newborn pups, and . . . suggest that the stress during fetal life induced by prenatal exposure to TiO_2 NPs could be implicated in depressive-like behaviors in adulthood."[142]

Impairing the antioxidant pathways means that the cells cannot protect themselves from the oxidation solar radiation causes, destroying the cells natural ability to protect themselves from sun damage.

How was this wrong path chosen? So many of our children are being diagnosed with mental disabilities, anxiety, and depression, could decades of ZnO and TiO_2 NPs have been contributing to this rise?

Chapter 7
DNA Damage – Alteration of Genomes on the Planet
(Changes In Gene Expressions – Impairs the Body's
Ability to Detox)

Octocrylene (OC) Creates 100s of DNA Alterations
OC exposure results in major impairment of the genes, with alterations in 628 DNA transcripts in the brain and 136 transcripts in the liver. Genetic replication is critical. Concern over losing this ability arises from a study that found OC mainly affects transcription of genes, impairing their expression related to developmental processes in the brain, and metabolism processes in the liver.[143]

ZnO NPs Alter DNA
Studies are revealing that ZnO NPs have the ability to alter a person's DNA. As ZnO NPs age, they undergo transformations that make them more harmful to our DNA, causing mutations or alteration of the DNA of mammalian (warm-blooded vertebrate) cells.[144] ZnO NPs induce concentration-dependent cellular toxicity, disrupt cell membranes, and cause DNA damage in rat primary nerve (neuronal) cells, and human connective tissue cells or fibroblasts.[145] These studies identify that older NPs and the greater number of NPs, the greater amount of harm they cause.

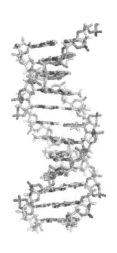

Researchers upon exposing white blood cells and adult mice to ZnO NPs identified DNA damage; including breaks, deletions, rearrangements, or additions to the DNA, and cellular toxicity to the white blood cells, as well as to the adult mice. The adult mice lost weight, exhibited passive behavior, and had reduced survival. They found severe DNA damage in peripheral blood and bone marrow cells. ZnO NPs also inhibited the mechanisms by which DNA repairs the damage that it undergoes. They found severe inflammation and damage to liver, lungs, and kidneys. Clarifying that it is the oxidation they create that causes the cellular damage, they found that the antioxidant N-acetyl cysteine significantly reduced the damage.[146]

MTHFR Genes Altered by TiO_2, ZnO, and BP3
Our body is designed to repair damage and provide detox pathways. Methylation is involved in many of these operations. The latest research clearly identifies that sunscreen chemicals affect the genes that are responsible for maintaining our body's healthy functioning. Exposure results in turning off the genes that help and switching on those that do not.

A gene-environment interaction occurs when the effect of an environmental exposure on health and behavior is conditional upon a person's genotype (or conversely, when environmental exposure alters genes, which have effects on health and behavior).[147] The study of these interactions is called epigenetics, which has become a new area of intense research, particularly when toxic chemicals that can alter genes are proliferating on the planet. A 2016 study adds TiO_2 and ZnO to a growing list of nanoparticles that could cause epigenetic (DNA) changes. Our bodies are designed to repair DNA when it is damaged. ZnO NPs not only damage DNA, but they also reduce the ability of the DNA to repair itself.

Many today are identifying they have various symptoms that are being connected to alterations in the MTHFR gene. ZnO NPs change the MTHFR gene, which is responsible for body-wide DNA methylation (adding a methyl group (CH3) to DNA, occurs in every cell in the body, and is essential in many reactions). Most importantly the methylation process assists in detoxing the body, and in the production of neurotransmitters. NPs lead to global DNA hypomethylation (less or reduced methylation) immediately after 24 hours of exposure. Notably, NPs are known to stimulate oxidative stress, which in turn is associated with gene hypomethylation. Epigenetic changes induced by NPs might be the earliest events of nano particle toxicity. After exposure to TiO_2 and ZnO NPs, the activity of the enzyme that is essential for DNA methylation (DNA methyltransferase) is reduced by 40%–50% in NP-exposed cells, leading to hypomethylation (less methylation) of DNA. These data provide more evidence that NPs, even at sub lethal concentrations, and at which no obvious cytotoxic effect or oxidative stress is manifested, still could create genetic reduction in DNA methylation.[148]

Another 2016 article concurs regarding the potential effects on health arise from nanomaterials and nanoparticles, and reduced DNA methylation diminishes the body's ability to detox and remove the toxins the body takes in daily. This is commonly found in autism spectrum disorders, ADHD, cognitive and behavioral issues, depression, anxiety, etc., all conditions that are experiencing large increases in numbers.[149]

Researchers have found that engineered nanomaterials (ENMs) like TiO_2 and ZnO kill as much as 15% of all cells. Exposure to levels that are being found in nature creates oxidative stress and alters DNA methylation in mammals' genes. They concluded this indicates that exposure to environmentally relevant concentrations of ENMs causes toxic changes at the cellular level that are able to alter the cells' DNA function, or its expression.[150]

ZnO is absorbed by lysosomes (vesicles inside cells containing digestive enzymes), which dissolve the ZnO that results in releasing zinc ions (Zn+). Zinc ions damage DNA. The amount of damage increases as the Zn+ concentration increases. ROS are generated, and the NPs decrease the ability of DNA to repair.[151]

Multiple studies have identified that NP exposure induces alterations in gene expression with altered proteins and toxicity. DNA hypomethylation can be associated with and explain the mechanism of NP toxicity and carcinogenicity for TiO_2 and ZnO NPs. The global hypomethylation is seen in a number of cancers, including thyroid, breast, cervical, prostate, stomach, lung, bladder, esophagus, colorectum, and liver.[152]

It is not just TiO_2 and ZnO that create this reduction in the ability of the body to methylate. A study published in 2018 in *Molecular Neurobiology* demonstrated that the use of BP3 at levels found at environmentally relevant concentrations also inhibited global DNA methylation and modifications of genes associated with neurodevelopmental abnormalities and/or neural degeneration, as well as cellular instability. The types of dysfunctions created are linked to neural degenerative diseases such as Alzheimer's disease, Parkinson's disease, Huntington's disease, encephalopathy, and amyotrophic lateral sclerosis – Lou Gehrig's disease or ALS.[153]

With so many conditions linked to mitochondrial dysfunction and deficient methylation, again it is time to consider that the mass use of sunscreens is a major contributing factor to the increases in disabling diseases we are experiencing today.

Chapter 8
Swimming Pools – Now
Toxic, Poison Filled Chemical Dumps

Small, urban swimming pools can contain significantly higher concentrations of sunscreen chemicals, which questions their safety for people using them, especially children.[154] Researchers state that swimming pool water is now a *sink* for UV-filters. With all the different chemicals found in sunscreens, people are now swimming in a sea of toxic chemicals.[155]

Exposure of sunscreen chemicals to chlorine can cause a decrease in their ability to absorb UV radiation, with a resultant loss of the UV protection they are promoted to provide, and they become increasingly toxic. When oxybenzone and dioxybenzone are chlorinated (mixed with pool water), they cause significantly more cell death than these individual chemicals when they have not been exposed to chlorine.[156]

In addition, UV filters have the potential to react with the chlorine and its disinfection-by-products (DBPs). Tragically, these combinations and their environmental fate have scarcely been addressed in environmental studies, allowing people to continue using sunscreens before entering swimming pools. A 2016 study identified that the sunscreen chemicals OMC and ODPABA (which are unstable in sunlight), combine with swimming pool chlorine disinfection-by-products, in the presence of sunlight, and create trihalomethanes, poisons that are associated with reproductive harm – being called a *mutagenic industrial chemical compound* that attacks DNA directly. They are toxic and carcinogenic, even at very low levels, and are associated with intestinal and bladder cancer, and along with affecting the reproductive system, they affect the liver, kidney, nervous systems.[157]

Thinking we are providing wholesome fun for children and protecting them from the sun has resulted in allowing them to swim in an unknown – untested mix of toxic chemicals that are poisonous – can harm their genetic make-up – and impair their ability to reproduce in the future.

It is time to stop harming our children and not allow sunscreens to be used before entering swimming pools, or any water environment, since so much research is revealing they cause harm to all species of life.

Chapter 9
Vitamin D and Sunshine's Multiple Health Benefits

The body uses your own skin as a production plant to produce its own very beneficial vitamin D3. Vitamin D3 performs many functions in the body, including cancer protection, maintaining and keeping bones strong, the heart healthy, promoting proper absorption of calcium and phosphorus, and helps to develop a strong immune system. Without it, we develop many of the symptoms that are becoming rampant in our society today: bone loss, hair loss, depression, fatigue, bone and back pain, impaired wound healing, muscle pain, and frequent infections. The conditions below are all associated with low vitamin D3 levels, and are undergoing rapid increases in incidence.

Dermatitis and eczema
ADHD
Autism
Lower back pain
High blood pressure: nitric oxide (NO)
Parkinson's disease
Osteoporosis
Rickets
Multiple sclerosis
Autoimmune diseases
Atherosclerosis
Obesity
Diabetes

Vitamin D Impacts the Body in Many Ways

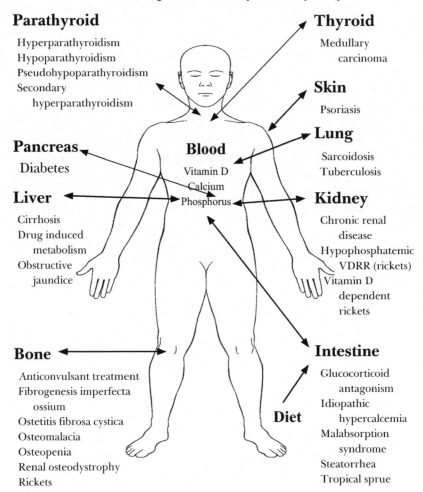

Parathyroid
Hyperparathyroidism
Hypoparathyroidism
Pseudohypoparathyroidism
Secondary
　hyperparathyroidism

Pancreas
Diabetes

Liver
Cirrhosis
Drug induced
　metabolism
Obstructive
　jaundice

Blood
Vitamin D
Calcium
Phosphorus

Thyroid
Medullary
　carcinoma

Skin
Psoriasis

Lung
Sarcoidosis
Tuberculosis

Kidney
Chronic renal
　disease
Hypophosphatemic
　VDRR (rickets)
Vitamin D
　dependent
　rickets

Bone
Anticonvulsant treatment
Fibrogenesis imperfecta
　ossium
Ostetitis fibrosa cystica
Osteomalacia
Osteopenia
Renal osteodystrophy
Rickets

Diet

Intestine
Glucocorticoid
　antagonism
Idiopathic
　hypercalcemia
Malabsorption
　syndrome
Steatorrhea
Tropical sprue

Figure 7.

Vitamin D not only protects from these conditions, but also protects from cancers. Research confirms that UVB radiation promotes the production of vitamin D3 in the skin, which significantly stops the formation of basal cell tumors. This finding made the investigators state that their research demonstrates the opposite conclusion of the established misbelief – the truth is that the sun's UV radiation actually has anti-basal cell cancer effects.[158]

Many researchers collectively came to the conclusion that the sun is beneficial and "should not be avoided." They participated in a medical conference entitled: Vitamin D for Public Health: Integrating Sunshine, Supplements and Measurement for Optimal Health. The conference was presented by Grassroots Health at the University of California San Diego to inform and to help initiate an action plan to restore a more balanced approach to solar radiation based on the collective input by the conference speakers. The following are conclusions from this seminar.

> "The current policy of sun avoidance is creating probable harm for the general population." . . . "The full solar spectrum is essential to optimal health and well-being. Humans are physiologically adapted to produce vitamin D in response to sun exposure, specifically UVB radiation; other regions of the spectrum seem to confer benefit as well. Though some vitamin D comes from our diet (and more recently from supplements), we should not ignore the natural capacity that we possess to produce our own. We are of the opinion that moderate sun exposure (less than the time required to burn) to the arms, shoulders, trunk, and legs should be sought rather than avoided. Once that limited time has been achieved, we agree that covering the skin or seeking shade may be appropriate. The benefits of such exposure go beyond production of vitamin D and include other physiological responses to sunlight, still inadequately explored, including release of nitric oxide, production of beta-endorphin, and regulation of circadian rhythms – all important components of life-long health and well-being."[159]

Sunshine Enhances

Nitric Oxide (NO) Production
Nitric oxide plays a critical role in blood pressure and overall circulation as it is a potent vasodilator that relaxes the arteries and expands the blood vessels, increasing blood flow, decreasing plaque growth, and decreasing blood clotting.

Beta-endorphins
Beta-endorphins are neurotransmitters in the brain that function to transmit electrical signals in both the central and peripheral nervous system, which reduce our perception of pain, acting similarly to drugs such as morphine and codeine. They trigger a positive feeling in the body, i.e., the feeling that follows a run or workout that many describe as *euphoric*.

Circadian Rhythm
Our circadian rhythm is critical to our well-being. In regulating many physiological processes, it is the *body clock* that tells our bodies when to sleep, rise, and eat. Sunlight is one of the environmental cues that helps regulate are internal clock, as its disruption causes a sleep disorder that can result in daytime sleepiness or depression.

All of these benefits are major reasons people flock to beaches and lakes. The sunshine makes them feel better.

Low Vitamin D Status In Humans

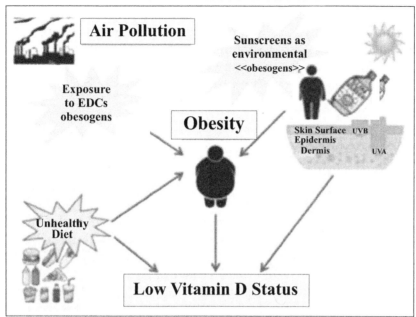

Figure 8. EDC = endocrine disrupting chemicals.

Source: Barrea L, Savastano S, Di Somma C, et al. Low serum vitamin
D-status, air pollution and obesity: A dangerous liaison. Rev *Endocr*
Metab Disord. 2017;18(2):207-214. Reprinted with permission.

A study published in 2018 detailed research that measured vitamin D levels in 903 adults who did not have diabetes, monitoring
them over a ten-year period. Those who had a vitamin D level
above 30 ng/ml had only one-third the incidence of diabetes as
those with 30 ng/ml. The value of vitamin D becomes even more
compelling, as they found an 80% reduced risk for diabetes in
those whose vitamin D was greater than 50 ng/ml.[160]

Obesity – Obesogens
There has been much emphasis on the increasing obesity among
Americans, however, sunscreen use can be one of the factors that is
creating the rise. The endocrine disruption makes the sunscreen
chemicals fall into a category called *obesogens*. Obesogens are

chemicals that alter pathways responsible for control of fat tissue development, increase the number of fat cells, alter metabolism, insulin sensitivity and lipid metabolism, resulting in a change in the set point that can result in the development of obesity. The study that published the figure on the previous page stated that there is a vicious cycle that is set up with low vitamin D, and an unhealthy diet.

Cholesterol Sulfate
Another critical function that sunshine on our skin performs for us is the formation cholesterol sulfate. Recent investigations have uncovered that it is sunshine on the skin that allows the body to create vitamin D3 sulfate and cholesterol sulfate. Cholesterol sulfate is being identified as an essential component in the health of the body. Among its many roles are the stabilization red blood cells, and reducing plaque formation in the arteries. To find out its numerous other roles, read the book: *Cindy and Erica's Obsession: To Solve America's Health Care Crisis*, which provides detailed descriptions of how this important component of sunshine assists the health of the body. It is available at:

www.newvoice.net/books

TiO2 Adsorbs Flame Retardants = Increasing Cellular Intake
In a 2018 study, researchers started looking at the interaction of chemicals with TiO2 due to its increasing prevalence in consumer products. Studying fish and an organophosphate flame retardant they found that TiO2 adsorbs the flame retardant, which then acts as a carrier that allows more of the chemical to be taken into the cells and tissues. They identified that the combination of these chemicals created decreases in the reproductive hormones – testosterone, estradiol (estrogen), follicle-stimulating hormone (FSH) and luteinizing hormone (LH) – inhibited egg production, and created significant developmental toxicity in the larvae, with adverse reproduction outcomes.[161]

If fish reproduction is harmed, the same must be happening to humans. Flame retardants are especially concerning since they were required by law for years to be in bedding and clothing, especially for our babies and children. This combined chemical mixture makes them more toxic. When we sit or sleep on furniture, beds, rugs, or wear clothing (children's sleepwear) we absorb them.

California's Governor Jerry Brown has revised a controversial law that he signed in 1975 during his first term as governor. On November 21, 2013, the law was changed after 35 years of harm. In its justification for the new rules, state officials cited studies suggesting that furniture foam treated with flame-retardant chemicals can actually be more hazardous in a fire. Officials of California's Bureau of Home Furnishings, which sets furniture standards, stated: "Flame retardant foam can actually increase smolder propensity."[162]

Even though the law has been modified and phased out on particular items, there are still many old items that would have the flame retardants in them. Cell phones and sunscreens were introduced in the 1970s. Let's hope that soon they will both be classified as toxic (as flame retardants have been found to be more harmful than beneficial), and be combined with promotions that discourage their use.

Chapter 10
Sunscreens' Ecological Harm to the Environment

Ecological harm to aquatic life is occurring throughout the world from both chemical EDs and the physical filters of ZnO and TiO2. "Benzophenone is harmful to aquatic organisms. Benzophenones in general have the environmentally critical properties of high lipophilicity (ability to dissolve into fats) and persistence, and are known to have adverse effects on the reproduction and hormonal functions of fish."[163]

In a 2015 article in *Science of the Total Environment,* researchers found sunscreen chemicals end up in river water, contaminating the plant and animal life that live in the rivers. They are found in tap and ground water, rivers, lakes, and ocean waters. Today, sunscreen chemicals are also found in many aquatic animals, especially in fish and mussels, crustaceans, mammals, and aquatic birds. This finding in most all samples tested is reasonable since wastewater treatment plants cannot remove sunscreen chemicals. These and other researchers also warn that environmental occurrences should be monitored more frequently and deeply.[164]

Researchers are identifying sunscreen chemicals as environmental pollutants since they are fat soluble, meaning they could accumulate within aquatic organisms, leading to their increasing burden through the food chain.[165] BP3 can be absorbed into fats, remains stable and does not breakdown from the sun. It is rapidly absorbed either orally or through the skin making it accumulate in tissues because it absorbs faster than it can be metabolized or excreted. Therefore, it accumulates in the body (e.g., it is bioaccumulative). BP3 metabolizes into other forms including benzophenone-1 (BP1), which has a longer biological half-life than BP3, which means it stays in the body longer than BP3. BP3 is now detected in the Earth's waters, soil, sediments, sludge, and all plant and animal life, including in the fish we eat.

This exposure has led to BP3 being detected in urine, serum, and breast milk samples world-wide, as well as BP1 being detected in the placenta.[166]

In Swiss rivers, higher concentrations of sunscreen chemicals are found in fish and in cormorants, suggesting food-chain accumulation.[167] Yet, manufacturers, knowing sunscreens would be used by people using our waterways, still incorporated them in their formulations. As a result, benzophenones are now found not only in rivers, lakes, and sea water, but also in tap water, which we bath in, cook with, and drink, and the groundwater, which grows our plants.[168]

Researchers in Spain analyzed various supplies of drinking water for five hormonally active sunscreen chemicals. They looked for benzophenone-3 (BP3), 3-(4-methylbenzylidene) camphor (4MBC), 2-ethylhexyl 4-(dimethylamino) benzoate (OD-PABA), 2-ethylhexyl 4-methoxycinnamate (EHMC) and octocrylene (OC). All 5 were detected in the water samples analyzed, including bottled mineral water, well water, and tap water even after being treated with an ion-exchange resin. This 2012 study identifies that people are now drinking the sunscreen chemicals society has been told are so essential to use, and also identifies how difficult it is to get these chemicals back out of the water.[169]

Sunscreen chemicals toxicity and ability to bioaccumulate (do not break down rapidly and stay in the life form increasing in concentration as larger species eat smaller ones) have made researchers look at ecological water habitats. In a 2017 article looking at watershed areas in Brazil, the researchers stated that sediments are a sink for sunscreen chemicals, the same as swimming pools now are.[170]

Coral Damage
Coral and algae live in a symbiotic relationship. Coral provides protection for the algae, while the algae provides the coral with vital oxygen that the algae manufactures from sunlight.

In 2008 scientists identified that even very low concentrations of the common sunscreen chemicals BP3, OMC, 4-MBC, and the preservative used in sunscreens, butyl paraben (BP), cause dormant viruses to reproduce, which kill the host algae, releasing the viruses and spreading the infection to nearby coral. Within 18-48 hours of exposure to the sunscreen, there was a release of large amounts of coral mucous that is composed of algae and coral tissue. Within 96 hours, the sunscreens caused a loss of the algae's membrane integrity and its photosynthesizing pigments, with a complete bleaching of the hard corals.[171] Exposure results in losing their gorgeous colors and becoming white.

Coral Samples Die Within 96 Hours after Exposure

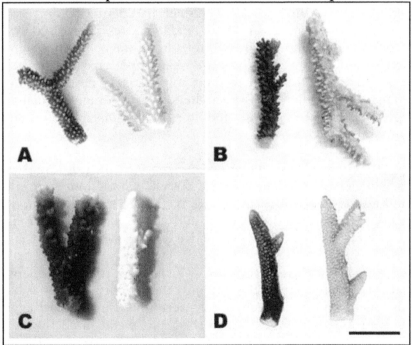

Figure 9.

Source: Danovaro R, Bongiorni L, Corinaldesi C, et al. Sunscreens cause coral bleaching by promoting viral infections. *Environ Health Perspect*. 2008. 116(4):441–447. Reprinted with permission.

This 2008 article proving sunscreens kill coral has not led to much alteration in changes in behavior. In 2016, coral reefs were still dying and BP3 was detected in coral reefs in the U.S. Virgin Islands and Hawaii.[172] Indeed, this is confirmed from multiple sources.

Studies have determined that octocrylene (OC) in cosmetics leads to contamination of the aquatic environment. Looking at the effects on adult fish and embryos, researchers found that OC bioaccumulates in fish.[173]

A 2014 study exposed freshwater snails due to their sensitivity to pollution in our aquatic ecosystem to two different concentrations of ZnO NPs for three weeks. The snails had significant decreases in glutathione, which assists with oxidative stress, decreased total protein and albumin, increased total lipids (fats) and cholesterol levels, and they had an increase in multiple enzymes in their blood (hemolymph) and in their soft tissues. These profound changes compelled the researchers to encourage regulatory agencies to more carefully monitor and regulate the use and disposal of ZnO NPs.[174]

In 2016, scientists studying octocrylene (OC) in fish found estrogenic changes in the ovaries, as well as both anti-estrogenic and anti-testosterone activity. Seeing these multiple hormonal actions, they warned that OC could accumulate in aquatic life disturbing cellular and reproductive development.[175]

Looking at wild bird species for seven types of sunscreen chemicals, researchers found that not only the parent compounds but also metabolites of the chemicals were found in the bird eggs. This means that the birds absorbed and metabolized the sunscreen chemicals before laying their eggs. They expressed concern about the effects this will have on the birds because these chemicals are capable of undergoing biomagnification, or increases in their concentrations occurring in higher species, across all species of birds.[176]

Looking at the possible contamination of nature preserve areas, researchers tested for BP sunscreens and their metabolites monitoring seven water sources around Shanghai. They found concentrations of all, but not related to recreational waters of swimmers contaminating from their bodies, but found higher concentration where there were areas of higher numbers of people.[177]

Protozoa exposed for 6 hours to an environmentally relatively low concentration of 4-MBC, and especially BP3, results in oxidation damage. Their results made the researchers state: It is imperative to further investigate the action of UV filters.[178]

Looking at a change in reactivity upon exposure to sunlight, researchers found that TiO_2 NPs are not toxic when UV radiation is blocked (meaning blocking the sun), but upon exposure to low intensity UV radiation they become toxic to marine phytoplankton (photoactive). The greater their concentration, the more they create stress on the phytoplankton causing decreased resiliency of marine ecosystems. They express concern due to the fact that the phytoplankton are the most important primary producers on Earth, and the beginning of the oceans' food chain. They stated all future research must consider phototoxicity when evaluating environmental impacts of nanomaterials, since many are photoactive.[179]

> Killing the bottom of the food chain will kill all life in the oceans, a major source of our food.

Investigating the effect of such a large amount of sunscreen formulations on the aquatic environment, zebrafish larvae and embryos were exposed to ZnO and TiO_2 in both the nanoparticle and bulk parent material. The investigators found serious tissue ulceration upon exposure to both ZnO NPs and to its bulk ZnO parent. Exposures of TiO_2 NPs, ZnO NPs and their bulk counterparts produced toxic effects on zebrafish embryos and larvae. They found that ZnO NPs are very toxic to zebrafish embryos and larvae. Sadly, even though ZnO was FDA approved in the U.S. as a sunscreen chemical in 1999, this 2008 article stated it was the "FIRST" study looking at the developmental toxicity of metal oxide nanoparticles, and included the warning that their findings highlight the importance of evaluating the potential toxicity to the environment of these manufactured nanoparticle materials.[180]

All these studies highlight the facts that sunscreen chemicals are toxic and disrupt normal reproduction and fetal development. Since these effects are found in all life forms investigated, we need to wake up to the reality that the sunscreen chemicals, rather than reducing our risk of skin cancers and melanoma, are threatening all life forms on the planet – and with alterations to the DNA – for generations to come.

The Beginnings of Change - Making a Difference

There is some hope. In 2018, Hawaii passed a law that would prohibit the sale and distribution of sunscreens that contain either benzophenone (BP3) or octinoxate (octyl methoxycinnamate, or OMC). This is a great first step. However, this is not going to go into effect until 2021, and is only limited to these two chemicals.[181]

A product that contains ZnO is now being promoted as a safe alternative for Hawaii, as it is not involved in coral death. However, documentation provided in this book proves that ZnO causes harm to all life, as it kills phytoplankton, it produces an equal amount of harm to ocean life.[182]

> It is important that everyone keep pressing for more laws, and hopefully there will soon be a law that will ban all the sunscreen chemicals from sale or distribution.

Eating better foods with high antioxidant content are the answer, rather than coating our skin with man-made toxic chemicals.

Chapter 11
Future Warnings:
New Ideas Being Considered Will Cause Harm as Well

There is research into using chemicals to prevent melanoma from forming. They do include diet and supplements, which if they include antioxidants these are great suggestions. However, they also are looking at NSAIDs (pain reducers) and statins (cholesterol lowering drugs).[183] These last two have problems themselves as current research has shown that neither of them are safe. Common side effects of NSAIDs are ulcers, kidney failure, and ringing in the ears. The side effects of statins are muscle loss (the heart is a muscle), reduced hormone levels, type 2 diabetes, and liver damage.

It is important for everyone to research the products that are brought to market and promoted for sunscreen use. This book provides plenty of evidence that manufacturers have not researched the chemicals they have been promoting as essential for humanity to use. We will also keep looking at products that are brought to market and include them in future editions of this book.

"Buyer beware!"

Chapter 12
Antioxidants:
Mother Nature's Safe and Natural Protective Sunscreens

There is a massive amount of evidence that proves antioxidant foods and supplements prevent and even reverse the oxidation damage solar radiation can create. There are many classes of antioxidants that have been studied in relation to protection from UV radiation. People who go into the sun after taking in high amounts of antioxidants report their skin does not even turn color, even those who have extremely white skin. High antioxidant foods are those with bright colors like reds, purples, and dark green. The antioxidants they contain are:

Anthocyanins
Beta-carotene
Carotenoids
Flavonoids
Polyphenols
Stilbenes
Tocopherols
Tocotrienols

"Based on the epidemiological evidence and laboratory studies conducted using in vitro [laboratory] and in vivo [in living tissue] systems, it is suggested that routine consumption or topical treatment of these polyphenols may provide efficient protection against the harmful effects of solar ultraviolet radiation in humans."[184]

A 2018 article in *Frontiers of Pharmacology* is even entitled: Natural Antioxidants: Multiple Mechanisms to Protect Skin from Solar Radiation. This is encouraging as it means that researchers are looking into healthful ways to protect us from solar radiation. They stated: "Growing body of research has been revealing a number of natural products with the ability to reduce most of the damaging effects of solar UVR exposure without causing significant cytotoxicity [cell damage and shrinking]."[185]

Just one antioxidant example: Garlic
Male rat pups given TiO_2 results in the atrophy of the testicles
(reduction in size). The antioxidant properties of aged garlic
extract has been shown to reduce this harm.[186]

There is plenty of research regarding the types of foods that
contain these beneficial antioxidants. How these antioxidants
interact and their degree of potency are listed in Chapter 17:
Antioxidants: Mother Nature's Protective Sunscreens in my
book: *Sunscreens Biohazard: Treat as Hazardous Waste*. Please go
to: www.SunscreensBiohazard.com In addition to the book,
there is a comprehensive food guide with a list of all the radiation
protective foods available at:

www.newvoice.net/diet-guide

Conclusions:
1. Research has not validated the continual drumbeat
    promoting the belief that the sun is not safe because it
    causes melanoma.
2. Sunshine provides many benefits for the whole body.
3. Sunscreen use actually promotes skin cancers.
4. Sunscreen chemicals are toxic to all systems in the body
    and to all life on the planet.
5. Blocking UVB radiation leads to low vitamin D3 levels
    due to the inability to produce this essential vitamin
    in the skin, which results in a multitude of health
    problems.
6. Do not buy products that have a SPF rating, or foods or
    clothing that contain titanium dioxide.
7. Eating, taking, or using antioxidants on the skin
    are natural, safe ways to protect the skin from solar
    radiation. Feeding the skin antioxidants provides
    nature's best solar radiation protection.
8. Remember that everything you place on your body will
    eventually find its way into your blood stream and be
    transported to your organs.
9. Continued use of these toxic chemicals has allowed
    them into your living and working environment, and to
    spread throughout the world.

The sunscreen fiasco described throughout this book highlights that government agencies like the U.S. FDA and Environmental Protection Agencies have not, and are not protecting us or the planet.

It is up to us to make better choices that impact our health. All life could depend on the decisions you make. The choice is ours to become informed, as everyone needs to become their own health advocate, and be stewards of all the precious life on our planet.

Resources

Ongoing Research and Updates
New Voice for Health Newsletter

We will be continually researching and finding the best make-ups, body lotions, sunning products, and antioxidants so that you can truly enjoy your time in the sun without worrying about cancerous changes or photoaging. As there are constantly new ideas and products emerging on the sunscreen market, the *New Voice for Health Newsletter* will provide the same critical examination and in-depth analysis of the studies and medical advice that you have seen throughout this book. Our goal is for you to have the clarity you need to make informed decisions as to whether utilizing the latest discovery is the right course of action for you and your family. It will provide information regarding the most current knowledge regarding:

NewsFlash

Health Information You Can Trust

Sunscreens' Multiple Links to Autism

Beware!
Pregnant Women – Infants – Children
Especially Females

Contained in this issue:
* Sunscreens Do Not Perform As Marketed
* UCLA & MIT Researchers Substantiate
  Sunscreens' Link to ADHD & Autism
* Toxic Chemical Disrupts Normal Nerve Cell
  Development in Brain
* Vitamin D Identified as Essential for Proper
  Nerve Cell Development
* Vitamin D Needed for Essential Brain Nerve
  Cell "Pruning"

This important newsletter will be published when critical-to-know information becomes available.

Resources

EMF Radiation Information and Remediation

EMF Radiations cause the same type of oxidation damage as sunscreens. We have found that there are many myths associated with whether cell phones and electronics are impacting our health.

> Cell phones and electronics are impacting our health in ways that may possibly be irreparable at the DNA level. We feel that the damage these devices are causing is as detrimental as sunscreens.

Another of our books in the

Breaking Away from the **MASS CONS**ciousness Series is:

EMF Freedom: Solutions for the 21st Century Pollution

It highlights the massive assault we are being bombarded with on a daily basis from the cell towers, cell phones, wireless devices, and the support services that were not available 40 years ago. We became aware of these being a problem when Elizabeth became EMF sensitive and had to find solutions that worked for her. What we found worked so well, we felt it was our obligation to offer the product line that helped her to offset the assault from wireless devices. See our ads on the next two pages.

Resources

EMF Products
Survival Solutions For Living In the Digital Age
Coverage For Cell Phones And
Wearable Technologies For Your Family:
energyDOTs and Baby Comforter

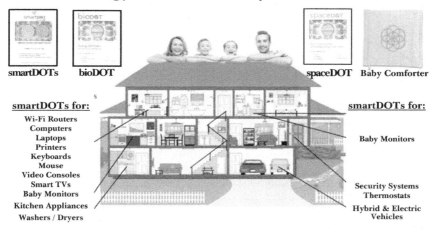

smartDOTs   bioDOT   spaceDOT   Baby Comforter

smartDOTs for:
Wi-Fi Routers
Computers
Laptops
Printers
Keyboards
Mouse
Video Consoles
Smart TVs
Baby Monitors
Kitchen Appliances
Washers / Dryers

smartDOTs for:

Baby Monitors

Security Systems
Thermostats
Hybrid & Electric
Vehicles

Make All Your Environments Safer from EMF!
Visit our Websites:

www.smartDOTs.us & www.EMFFreedom.com

21st Century Health Consulting LLC (our parent company) offers products that assist with EMF radiation, and will be continually upgrading its product line as technology changes and new devices become available. As the needs change, with stronger wireless communications continuing to be installed in communities around the world, our commitment is to act on your behalf seeking out and offering only the "best products available."

See the next page for the available scientific studies.

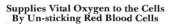

Resources

EMF Products

3 Scientific Methods Show the Healthful Effects from engeryDOTs

Supplies Vital Oxygen to the Cells By Un-sticking Red Blood Cells (allows them to flow freely throughout body)	Strengthens the Body's Bio Field To Reduce the EMF Impact (allowing less EMF to penetrate)	Reduces Inflammation (significantly reduced)

       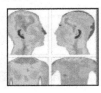

Before   1 Hour   smartDOTs   1 Hour   Before   After   Before   After
         on cell   added   with
         (no device)   to cell   smartDOTs

These products are CE certified as a Class 1 Medical Device by the European Union for distribution throughout the EU.

These products and statements have not been evaluated by the FDA.

The full scientific studies can be viewed at:

Blood analysis at: www.newvoice.net/blood

Bio Field and Inflammation at: www.newvoice.net/biofield

Elizabeth Plourde, C.L.S., NCMP, Ph.D.
Marcus Plourde, Ph.D.
www.smartDOTs.us
marcus@newvoice.net

Appendix A

⸰ Protecting Yourself – Naturally
(Reprinted from *Sunscreens BioHazard: Treat as Hazardous Waste*)

The concerns that this book covers are beginning to be voiced by the medical community. In the physicians Web-based medical information news, *Medscape*, an article about sunscreen and its use was concluded with: "However, further research is needed in many areas including the role of visible light, the risks of systemic absorption of sunscreen agents, and the role of vitamin D and sun exposure in preventing cancers and other diseases."[187]

Until these areas are clarified, it is critical for everyone to take steps that will protect the skin with natural ways that do not create more harm than good.

Australian SunSmart® Program
There has been a growing concern that advice to use sunscreen may lead to longer sun exposure once *protection* is applied, which counteracts the reasons for the utilization of sunscreens. In 1982, the Australian government instituted what they called the SunSmart program, intended to reduce UV exposure, and increase use of protective clothing, hats, sunglasses, and sunscreen. Television advertisements were aimed at changing attitudes about sun tanning, and for acceptance of wearing more protective attire of *neck to knee* swimsuits for children. Due to the program, there was an increase in sun-protective behavior between 1987-2002, which correlated to a reduction in the incidence for melanoma rates in younger children. Below are their recommendations.

"However, sunscreen should not be used as the sole method of sun protection nor as a means for extending the amount of time spent in the sun. The best way for individuals to lower their risk of skin cancer is to reduce their sun exposure by combining all strategies:

> Staying out of the sun between the peak burning hours of 10 AM to 2 PM; seeking shade or bringing it (for example, a beach umbrella or tent); and wearing hats and other protective clothing, like long sleeve T-shirts and lightweight pants."

"'Building comprehensive approaches to reducing sun exposure, not just using sunscreen, are necessary to achieve our goals of reducing the burden of skin cancer.' It is not too late to cover up when in the sun and enjoy the outdoors this summer."[188]

Australia's Requirements for Labeling Sunscreens

The Australian government's Therapeutic Goods Administration (TGS) wording regarding sunscreen labeling requires that it include the urging of avoiding prolonged sun exposure and advising to wear protective clothing. The required wording is:

> "If (and only if) a therapeutic sunscreen has an SPF of 30+ and it provides broad spectrum protection, the label is permitted to include a representation to the effect that the product *may assist in preventing some skin cancers* or *may reduce the risk of some skin cancers* provided the label also highlights the need for avoidance of prolonged exposure to the sun and the importance of wearing protective clothing, hats and eye wear. Other acceptable related claims are *can aid in the prevention of solar keratoses* and *can aid in the prevention of sunspots*."[189]

U.S. FDA 2011 Guidelines for Labeling Sunscreens
June 14, 2011, the U.S. FDA published new guidelines that outline their current recommendations. The main points in regards to labeling are listed below.

- The new regulations became effective summer 2012.
- In order to state on the label SPF 15 to a maximum of SPF 50, product has to pass a "broad spectrum" test showing that it protects against both UVA and UVB.
- If broad spectrum, claim can be made that the product protects against skin cancer and early skin aging, as well as against sunburn, if it is used as directed along with other sun protective measures:
    o Limit time in sun between 10 AM and 2 PM.
    o Wear protective clothing: long-sleeved shirts, pants, sunglasses, and broad-brimmed hats.
- If it does not protect against both UVA and UVB, it can only state a SPF value (cannot say broad spectrum) and only claim protection against sunburn.
- Maximum SPF of 50 allowed to be claimed as there is no sufficient data to show that products provide protection greater than SPF 50.
- Cannot claim protection unless reapplied every 2 hours.
- If water resistant: claims must state on front of label that it remains effective for 40 minutes or 80 minutes while swimming or sweating.
- If not water resistant must include a direction instructing consumers to use a water resistant sunscreen if swimming or sweating.
- Label cannot claim "waterproof" "sweat proof" or "sunblock" as this overstates their effectiveness.

The government agencies that are regulating sunscreens in their efforts to protect us recognize that reducing prolonged sun exposure and covering our bodies are essential even when they recommend sunscreen use.

There are many actions that can be taken that do not expose you, your family, or the planet to detrimental toxic chemical harm.

What You Can Do
To Protect Yourself and Your Family

Learn and Follow the UV Index
There is a UV Index that provides a rating of how strong the
radiation of the sun will be on an hourly and daily basis world-
wide. The UV radiation strength is strongest between 10 AM
to 2 PM. As much as 80% of UV rays pass through clouds, so
still take the same precautions on cloudy days as you would on
bright, sunny days. For the index rating for your local area you
can type in your city and country or state, or your ZIP code at
either of the two Websites that are listed below:

World-wide the UV index can be accessed at:
www.uvawareness.com/uv-forecast/index.php

In the U.S., the National Weather Service issues a daily forecast
of UV intensity that can be accessed at:
www.epa.gov/sunwise/uvindex.html

The rating scale they both use is listed in the box below.

UV Index Rating System

Rating	Exposure Level
<3	Low
3 to 5	Moderate
6 to 7	High
8 to 10	Very high
11+	Extreme

Table 3.

Source: EPA Website. Sunscreen: The Burning Facts. Available at:
www.epa.gov/sunwise/doc/sunscreen.pdf

The lower UV Index numbers would allow more sun exposure,
while it is best to cover up or stay out of the sun when the index
climbs to High Exposure Level and above.

Do Not Use Artificial Sun Tanning Salons

In reviewing the statistics of types of cancers among men and women and those who utilize sun tanning beds, a study published in 2007 reveals that the artificial radiation of sun tanning beds increases the risk of basal cell carcinoma, but not melanoma. However, there was not enough data to identify whether squamous cell skin cancers would be affected, but it would be best not to risk basal cell cacinomas.[190]

Do Not Use Either Spray-on or Airbrush Tanning Products

There are so many ingredients in the formulations that are being marketed to artificially darken the skin that it is impossible to cover all of them here. Most do contain a form of acetone, dihydroxyacetone (DHA), which even though it is considered relatively non-toxic can cause drying and irritation of the skin. Many of them only last about a week and then have to be reapplied, adding to the problem of continual drying of the skin. The most important thing in their regard to know is that the changes they create in the skin to cause the tanning can act like sunscreens, which reduces the formation of vitamin D and leads to lower body-wide vitamin D levels.[191]

Know the Medications that Increase Susceptibility to UV Rays

Certain medications increase the susceptibility to burning from the UV rays. The medications listed below increase burning with sun exposure. If you are taking any of the listed medications, do take extra care to stay protected from the sun.[192]

Always:
    Fluoroquinolones
    Sulfonamides
    Tetracyclines (especially demeclocycline)
Less frequently:
    Doxycycline
    Oxytetracycline

Rarely:
> Minocycline
> Thiazide diuretics
> Furosemide
> Amiodarone
> Sulfonylureas
> Acetazolamide (diamox)
> Phenothiazines
> Nonsteroidal anti-inflammatory drugs (naproxen, ibuprofen, aspirin)

Identify True Sun Allergies

For those who have allergic reactions to the sun, first make sure that it is not an allergy to any sunscreen lotion or body lotion that you may have applied. For some individuals an allergic reaction can occur with many of the sunscreen ingredients, particularly upon exposure to the sun. When you have determined that it is from the sun, the immune system needs to be addressed. It could be there is a toxic build up in the body or heavy metal poisoning of the liver. To rule this out, seek a doctor's help for toxin removal.

Action Steps to Take

Rather than use chemicals, there are many steps you can take to protect yourself from UV rays.

- Seek shade, cover up, and avoid the sun between 10 AM and 2 PM.
- Be extra careful when the UV Index is high.
- Be extra careful near water, snow, and sand as they reflect and intensify the radiation.
- Do not use sun tanning products or tanning beds.

Know What You Put on Your Body and into Your Body

The biochemistry of the body is extremely complicated, to say the least. Know what you are putting on your skin, the largest organ of your body, as it readily and rapidly absorbs what is put on it. Read every label for body lotions, cosmetics, clothing, and swimwear. When they state a rating for UV protection, find out what chemicals have been used for the protection, as sun filtering chemicals including TiO_2 are appearing in many products. One of the authors of the 2009 UCLA *Cancer Research* article on TiO_2 nanoparticles stated:

> "The manufacture of TiO_2 nanoparticles is a huge industry," Dr. Schiestl said, ". . . with production at about 2 million tons per year. In addition to paint, cosmetics, sunscreen and vitamins, the nanoparticles can be found in toothpaste, food colorants, nutritional supplements and hundreds of other personal care products." He voiced his concern over these products due to his UCLA study that lead to the conclusions: "In the past, these TiO_2 nanoparticles have been considered non-toxic in that they do not incite a chemical reaction. Instead, it is surface interactions that the nanoparticles have within their environment – in this case inside a mouse – that is causing the genetic damage, Schiestl said. They wander throughout the body causing oxidative stress, which can lead to cell death."[193]

Even when the product is not advertised that it is for sun protection, still read the labels. Read all the over-the-counter medications as TiO_2 nanoparticles are added to some (e.g., Benadryl®). Also read every label in natural health food stores. Pure and natural soaps with only a handful of ingredients can still contain TiO_2, which will be in the nanoparticle form even though they are not required to include that information on the label.

Products containing TiO_2 nanoparticles are being promoted for everything. It is "Buyer Beware." Websites have cropped up promoting them as safe and even that they are for a greener planet. Everything, from self-cleaning toilets, deodorant bars, air purifiers, and water filters, to paint, have had these minute particles added. They are not safe or good for the planet; they are not only hazardous to your health, they are hazardous to the health of the planet. Check the labels on everything you buy and refuse to buy products that incorporate either TiO_2 or ZnO nanoparticles. When there is no market for their products, the manufacturers will stop utilizing them.

Throw Sunscreen Chemicals in Hazardous Waste Stations
Read the labels of all of your skin care products. Throw out all of those that include any of the chemicals listed in this book. Make sure to dispose of them in your community's hazardous waste area and not into the main garbage, as they need to be removed from the environment.

Select Sun Shielding Clothes
Select tightly woven fabrics. To determine whether clothing can block the sun's rays, it can be held up to the light to determine whether light is coming through it or not. A good material for blocking the rays is tightly knit denim.

Sun protective behavior can become part of our lives again. Umbrellas can be used for shade. An umbrella with tightly women fabric would provide protection, and is a better choice for your health than those that are being manufactured with TiO2 nanoparticles. Women can start making the wearing of gloves fashionable again, just like it was only 50 short years ago. Swimming attire that covers more of the body, especially for our children and babies like the campaign on Australian television, can also become the new *normal* for sensible sun behavior.

Reduce the Amount of Time Spent in the Sun
There are common sense answers for everything, including our sunbathing behavior. There needs to be a balance to everything. Sunscreens have created a false sense of security. We were not designed to stay in the sun as long as sunscreens have allowed us to by blocking out our red warning light – a sunburn. By doing so, we have artificially stopped a natural protection process.

Avoid Commercial Chemical and Physical Sunscreens
At the time of this writing, I have not discovered any products that claim sunscreen protection that do not incorporate at least one of the chemicals, or the physical blockers that have been identified in this book as being harmful for humans as well as for the planet. They are products that were put on the market without adequate testing. We cannot chemically treat ourselves without disrupting the body's ecosystem, and the environmental ecosystem of the planet's lakes, rivers, and oceans.

Adopt Antioxidants

Adopt antioxidants in your diet and for your skin as a way of life. They not only will protect your skin, they will generate health throughout your body. They are especially essential for our survival in today's toxin filled world.

> Do not use the clothing that advertises an SPF rating by using a sunscreen product like TiO2 to block the sun. It will be absorbed into the skin of the wearer, and washes completely out into our water systems in about 20 washes.

Call to Action

The perceptions of the sun's potential for cancerous changes and creating damage that leads to skin aging have been utilized as the impetus to elicit cooperation of protecting the skin with sunscreen preparations. The call to action today needs to be turned toward protecting life on the planet as we know it. For the health of our bodies and developing babies, and for survival of both fresh and salt water fish, we humans have to stop using all these sunscreen preparations and switch to nature's sunscreens – the antioxidants. Utilize clothing that covers our bodies and stay out of the sun as our ancestors used to before sunscreens allowed us to circumvent our warning sunburn and encouraged us to stay in the sun much longer than is healthy for our skin.[194]

These concerns and proof of harm to life have shown up throughout the entire lifetime of sun filtering products being offered to consumers. Yet warning labels have not been required and the manufacturers have not volunteered to pull them off the market in concern of the safety of human beings and preservation of the aquatic and marine life on the planet. However, this lack of response threatens our very existence on the planet, because if our oceans die off – humankind will not be far behind. It is imperative that we only use products that protect our health, our unborn children's brains and natural sexual development, and preserve the incredible array of life in the ocean that feeds us and sustains us, and provides such a great playground for our enjoyment.

Appendix B

Synonyms for Benzophenone-3

Trade Names:
Advastab 45;
Anuvex; b3;
Benzophenone;
Cyasorb UV;
HMB;
NCI-C60957;
NSC-7778;
Oxybenzone
Spectra-sorb UV;
Syntase 62;
UF 3;
USAF CY-9;
Uvinul M 40;

Chemical names:
4-methoxy-2-hydroxy-benzophenone;
2-hydroxy-4-methoxyphenyl)phenyl-methanone;
2-hydroxy-4-methoxyphenyl;
2-benzoyl-5-methoxyphenol;
2-hydroxy-4-methoxybenzophenone;
4-08-00-02442 (Beilstein handbook reference) 8271
Ai3-23644;

Source: Environmental Working Group (EWG) Website. Skin Deep Cosmetics Database. Available at: www.ewg.org/skindeep/ingredient/704372/OXYBENZONE/#.Wx9OIGXnsUN. Retrieved June 11, 2018.

ASL 24;
Aduvex 24;
Chimassorb 90;
Escalol 567;

Eusolex 4360;
Kemisorb 11;
MOB;
Neo Heliopan BB;
Ongrostab HMB;
Onzone;
Oxybenzon;
Seesorb 101;
Spectra-Sorb UV 9;
Sumisorb 110;
Sunscreen UV 15;
Tinosorb B 3;
UV 9;
Uvinul 3040;
Uvinul 9;
Viosorb 110.

Source: Toronto Research Chemicals Website. Oxybenzone. Available at: www.trc-canada.com/product-detail/?O867300. Retrieved June 11, 2018.

Cyasorb UV 9;
Cyasorb UV 9 Light absorber.

Source: Google Books Website. The National Toxicology Program's Chemical Data Compendium, Volume 1. Available at:https://books.google.com/books?id=rQY0oOZxAUgC&pg=PA489&lpg=PA489&dq=USAF+CY-9&source=bl&ots=7yzWYLDdD3   &sig=CSAp-e7BOEOu4gT3MaZylIX9LTc&hl=en&sa=X&ved=0ahUKEwiLm6m3o83bAhVDL6wKHRWsDZwQ6AEIeDAI#v=onepage&q=USAF%20CY-9&f=false. Retrieved June 11, 2018.

COLIPA N° S38;
Uvasorb MET/C
Uvistat 24. 8274

Source: European Commission: Health & Consumer Protection - Directorate-General Website. Opinion on Benzonphenone-3 Colipa N° S38. Available at: https://ec.europa.eu/health/ph_risk/committees/04_sccp/docs/sccp_o_078.pdf. Retrieved June 11, 2018.

Picture Credits

Cover: Background: 123rf.com/profile_Satina
    Family: 123rf.com/Cathy Yeulet
    Coral: 123rf.com/profile_ Frantisek Hojdysz
    Polaroid: 123rf.com/profile_Maria Tkach

Page #s

30 Skin - UVB: Educational Technology Clearinghouse. Available at: http://etc.usf.edu/. Retrieved July 9, 2011.
30 Skin - UVA: Educational Technology Clearinghouse. Available at: http://etc.usf.edu/. Retrieved July 9, 2011.
30 Skin - IR: Educational Technology Clearinghouse. Available at: http://etc.usf.edu/. Retrieved July 9, 2011.
49 Mother nursing: 123rf.com/profile_Famveldman57
    DDT Advertisement 1947: 123rf .com/profiles_Goodluz/ Alexraths/Robert_Przbysz/Andrey_Kekyalyaynen/Smileus/ Wollwerth/Keith_Homan/
    Advertisement *Time* magazine June 30, 1947
61 Spray sunscreens: 123rf.com/profile_famveldman/profile_ tkphotography/
87 DNA strand: Wikimedia Commons/Richard Wheeler
92 Kids in pool: 123rf.com/profile_yobro10
94 Body: istock.com/profile_Harley_McCabe
111 Globe: 123rf.com/profile_gf-jpeg_8056970
115 Advertisement: 123rf.com/profile_Dominicogelermo/ profile_pixetfritter/
    Products: Phi Harmonics Ltd. - Reprinted with permission.
116 Science illustrations: Phi Harmonics Ltd. - Reprinted with permission.

References

1. CDC Website. MMWR: Guidelines for School Programs to Prevent Skin Cancer. Available at: www.cdc.gov/mmwr/preview/mmwrhtml/rr5104a1.htm. Retrieved January 28, 2018.

2. CDC Website. Changes Over Time: Melanomas of the Skin. Available at: www.cdc.gov/cancer/skin/statistics/trends.htm. Retrieved January 28, 2018.

   Note: Page changed by October, 2018. This Website has the same statistics that were on the January 2018 CDC Web page. Available at: www.skinvision.com/articles/melanoma-facts-the-current-situation

   Guy GP, Thomas CC, Thompson T, Watson M, Massetti GM, Richardson LC. Vital Signs: Melanoma Incidence and Mortality Trends and Projections — United States, 1982–2030. *MMWR Morb Mortal Wkly Rep.* 2015 Jun 5; 64(21):591–596. Available at: www.ncbi.nlm.nih.gov/pmc/articles/PMC4584771/. Retrieved October 29, 2018.

3. Chemical & Engineering News (C&EN) Website. Relsch MS. After More than a Decade, FDA Still Won't Allow New Sunscreens. Available at: https://cen.acs.org/articles/93/i20/Decade-FDA-Still-Wont-Allow.html. Retrieved January 28, 2018.

4. ASCO University Website. Mitsis DKL, Groman A, Beaupin LM, et al. Trends in demographics, incidence, and survival in children, adolescents and young adults (AYA) with melanoma: A Surveillance, Epidemiology and End Results (SEER) population-based analysis. Presentation 2015 ASCO Annual Meeting – Monday, June 1, 2015. Available at: https://meetinglibrary.asco.org/record/112435/abstract. Retrieved January 28, 2018.

5. Kaidbey KH. Again PP, Sack RM, et al: Photoprotection by melanin–a comparison of black and Caucasian skin. *J Am Acad Dermatol.* 1979;1:249-260.

6. Council on Scientific Affairs: Harmful effects of ultraviolet radiation. *JAMA* 1989;262:380-384.

7. Wolf P, Donawho CK, Kripke ML. Effect of sunscreens on UV radiation-induced enhancement of melanoma growth in mice. *J Natl Cancer Inst.* 1994 Jan 19;86(2):99-105.

8. Fenske NA, Koo J. R3: Effect of sunscreens on UV radiation-induced enhancement of melanoma growth in mice. *J Natl Cancer Inst.* 1994 Jan 19;86(18):1425-1426.

9. Garland CF, Garland FC, Gorham ED. Re: Effect of Sunscreens on UV Radiation-Induced En-hancement of Melanoma Growth in Mice. *J Natl Cancer Inst.* 1994 May; 86(10);798-9.

   Hunter D. Colditz G, Stampfer M, et al: Risk factors for basal cell carcinoma in a prospective cohort of women. *Ann Epidemiol. 1990;*1:13-23.

10. Kripke ML, Donawho CK, Wolf P. Response to Re: Effect of sunscreens on UV radiation-induced enhancement of melanoma growth in mice. *J Natl Cancer Inst.* 1994;86(10):799.

11. Garland CF, Garland FC, Gorham ED. Re: Effect of Sunscreens on UV Radiation-Induced Enhancement of Melanoma Growth in Mice. *J Natl Cancer Inst.* 1994;86(10):798-799.

12. Berwick M, Erdei E, Hay J. Melanoma epidemiology and public health. *Dermatol Clin.* 2009 Apr;27(2):205-214, viii.

13. Perera E, Gnaneswaran N, Staines C, Win AK, Sinclair R. Incidence and prevalence of non-melanoma skin cancer in Australia: A systematic review. *Australas J Dermatol.* 2015 Nov;56(4):258-267.

14. Moshammer H, Simic S, Haluza D. UV-Radiation: From Physics to Impacts. *Int J Environ Res Public Health.* 2017 Feb 17;14(2). pii: E200.

15. Ruszkiewicz JA, Pinkas A, Ferrer B, Peres TV, Tsatsakis A, Aschner M. Neurotoxic effect of active ingredients in sunscreen products, a contemporary review. *Toxicol Rep.* 2017 May 27;4:245-259.

16. Gorham ED, Mohr SB, Garland CF, Chaplin G, Garland FC. Do sunscreens increase risk of mela-noma in populations residing at higher latitudes? *Ann Epidemiol.* 2007 Dec;17(12):956-963.

17. Linos E, Keiser E, Fu T, Colditz G, Chen S, Tang JY. Hat, shade, long sleeves, or sunscreen? Rethinking US sun protection messages based on their relative effectiveness. *Cancer Causes Control.* 2011;22(7):1067-1071.

18. Chemical & Engineering News (C&EN) Website. Relsch MS. After More than a Decade, FDA Still Won't Allow New Sunscreens. Available at: https://cen.acs.org/articles/93/i20/Decade-FDA-Still-Wont-Allow.html. Retrieved January 28, 2018.

19. Chemical & Engineering News (C&EN) Website. Relsch MS. After More than a Decade, FDA Still Won't Allow New Sunscreens. Available at: https://cen.acs.org/articles/93/i20/Decade-FDA-Still-Wont-Allow.html. Retrieved January 28, 2018.

19. Science Direct Website. Avobenzone. Available at: www.sciencedirect.com/topics/pharmacology-toxicology-and-pharmaceutical-science/avobenzone. Retrieved June 21, 2018.

20. Waring RH, Harris RM. Endocrine disrupters: a human risk? *Mol Cell Endocrinol.* 2005 Dec 1;244(1-2):2-9.

21. Krause M, Klit A, Blomberg Jensen M, Søeborg T, Frederiksen H, Schlumpf M, Lichtensteiger W, Skakkebaek NE, Drzewiecki KT. Sunscreens: are they beneficial for health? An overview of endocrine disrupting properties of UV-filters. *Int J Androl.* 2012 Jun;35(3):424-436.

22. Fisher Scientific Website. Material Safety Data Sheet Benzophenone. Available at: https://fscimage.fishersci.com/msds/02740.htm. Retrieved October 29, 2018.

23. CDC Website. National Biomonitoring Program. Available at: www.cdc.gov/biomonitoring/index.html. Retrieved June 21, 2018. CDC Website. Benzophenone-3 (BP-3) Factsheet. Available at: www.cdc.gov/biomonitoring/Benzophenone-3_FactSheet.html. Retrieved November 26, 2017

24. Krause M, Andersson AM, Skakkebaek NE, Frederiksen H. Exposure to UV filters during sum-mer and winter in Danish kindergarten children. *Environ Int.* 2017 Feb;99:177-184.

24a. No authors listed. Toxicology and carcinogenesis studies of benzophenone (CAS No. 119–61–9) in F344/N rats and B6C3F1 mice (feed studies). *Natl Toxicol Program Tech Rep Ser.Natl Toxicol Program Tech Rep Ser.* 2006;(533):1-264. PMID:16741556. As cited in IARC Monographs on the Evaluation of Carcinogenic Risks to Humans, No. 101. *IARC Working Group on the Evaluation of Carcinogenic Risk to Humans.* Lyon (FR): International Agency for Research on Cancer; 2013. Available at: www.ncbi.nlm.nih.gov/books/NBK373188/. Retrieved: October 30, 2018.

National Library of Medicine / NIH Website. HSDB (2010). Benzophenone. Hazardous substance database. 2010. Available at: http://toxnet.nlm.nih.gov/. As cited in IARC Monographs on the Evaluation of Carcinogenic Risks to Humans, No. 101. *IARC Working Group on the Evaluation of Carcinogenic Risk to Humans.* Lyon (FR): International Agency for Research on Cancer; 2013. Available at: www.ncbi.nlm.nih.gov/books/NBK373188/. Retrieved: October 30, 2018.

25. California OEHHA Website. Proposition 65 Law and Regulations. Available at: https://oehha.ca.gov/proposition-65/law/proposition-65-law-and-regulations. Retrieved July 15, 2018.

26. Liebert MA. Final Report on the Safety Assessment of Benzophenones-1, 3, 4, 5, 9, and 11. *J Am Coll Toxicol.* 1983;2(5)35-77.

French JE. NTP technical report on the toxicity studies of 2-Hydroxy-4-methoxybenzophenone (CAS No. 131-57-7) Administered Topically and in Dosed Feed to F344/N Rats and B6C3F1 Mice. *Toxic Rep Ser.* 1992;21:1-E14. Available at: https://ntp.niehs.nih.gov/ntp/htdocs/st_rpts/tox021.pdf. Retrieved June 23, 2018.

27. Axelstad, M.; Boberg, J.; Hougaard, K.S.; Christiansen, S.; Jacobsen, P.R.; Mandrup, K.R.; Nel-lemann, C.; Lund, S.P.; Hass, U. Effects of pre- and postnatal exposure to the UV-filter octyl methox-ycinnamate (OMC) on the reproductive, auditory and neurological development of rat offspring. *Toxicol Appl Pharmacol.* 2011, 250, 278–290.

28. Blüthgen N, Meili N, Chew G, Odermatt A, Fent K. Accumulation and effects of the UV-filter octocrylene in adult and embryonic zebrafish (Danio rerio). *Sci Total Environ.* 2014 Apr 1;476-477:207-217.

Zhang QY, Ma XY, Wang XC, Ngo HH. Assessment of multiple hormone activities of a UV-filter (octocrylene) in zebrafish (Danio rerio). *Chemosphere.* 2016 Sep;159:433-441.

29. Klinubol P, Asawanonda P, Wanichwecharungruang SP. Transdermal penetration of UV filters. *Skin Pharmacol Physiol.* 2008. 21(1):23-29.

30. Armeni T, Damiani E, Battino M, Greci L, Principato G. Lack of in vitro protection by a common sunscreen ingredient on UVA-induced cytotoxicity in keratinocytes. *Toxicology.* 2004. 203(1-3):165-178.

31. California OEHHA Website. Proposition 65 Law and Regulations. Available at: https://oehha.ca.gov/proposition-65/law/proposition-65-law-and-regulations. Retrieved July 15, 2018.

32. Wang SQ, Lim HW. Current status of the sunscreen regulation in the United States: 2011 Food and Drug Administrations's final rule on labeling and effectiveness testing. Available at: www.saviderm.com/posters-newsletters/2017/june/wang%20JAAD%20final%20rule%20sunscreen%20labeling.pdf. Retrieved June, 4, 2018.

33. Ozáez I, Aquilino M, Morcillo G, Martínez-Guitarte JL. UV filters induce transcriptional changes of different hormonal receptors in Chironomus riparius embryos and larvae. *Environ Pollut.* 2016 Jul;214:239-247.

34. Schlumpf M, Durrer S, Faass O, et al. Developmental toxicity of UV filters and environmental exposure: a review. *Int J Androl.* 2008;31(2):144-151.

35. Rehfeld A, Dissing S, Skakkebaek NE. Chemical UV Filters Mimic the Effect of Progesterone on Ca2 + Signaling in Human Sperm Cells. *Endocrinology.* 2016 Nov;157(11):4297-4308.

    Axelstad M, Hass U, Scholze M, Christiansen S, Kortenkamp A, Boberg J. EDC Impact: reduced sperm counts in rats exposed to human relevant mixtures of endocrine disrupters. *Endocr Connect.* 2018;7(1):139-148.

    Ruszkiewicz JA, Pinkas A, Ferrer B, Peres TV, Tsatsakis A, Aschner M. Neurotoxic effect of active ingredients in sunscreen products, a contemporary review. *Toxicol Rep.* 2017;4:245-259.

36. Wang J, Pan L, Wu S, et al.. Recent advances on endocrine disrupting effects of UV filters. *Int J Environ Res. Public Health.* 2016;13(8):782.

    Maipas S, P. Nicolopoulou-Stamati P. Sun lotion chemicals as endocrine disruptors. *Hormones* (Athens). 2015;14:32–46.

    Ponzo OJ, Silvia C, Evidence of reproductive disruption associated with neuroendocrine changes induced by UV-B filters, phthalates and nonylphenol during sexual maturation in rats of both gender, *Toxicology.* 2013;311:41–51.

37. Axelstad M, Hass U, Scholze M, Christiansen S, Kortenkamp A, Boberg J. EDC IMPACT: Reduced sperm counts in rats exposed to human relevant mixtures of endocrine disrupters. *Endocr Connect.* 2018 Jan;7(1):139-148.

38. Dareer SM, Kalin JR, Tillery KF, Hill DL. Disposition of HMB in rats dosed orally, intravenously, or topically. J *Toxicol Environ Health*. 1986;19(4):491-502.

39. French JE. NTP technical report on the toxicity studies of 2-Hydroxy-4-methoxybenzophenone (CAS No. 131-57-7) Administered Topically and in Dosed Feed to F344/N Rats and B6C3F1 Mice. *Toxic Rep Ser*. 1992;21:1-E14. Available at: https://ntp.niehs.nih.gov/ntp/htdocs/st_rpts/tox021.pdf. Retrieved June 23, 2018.

40. Dareer ELSM, Kalin RJ, Tillery KF, Hill DL, Disposition of 2-hydroxy-4-methoxybenzophenone in rats dosed orally, intravenously, or topically. *J Toxicol Environ Health*. 1986;19:491–502.

    Kadry AM, Okereke CS, Abdel-Rahman MS, Friedman MA, Davis RA, Pharmacokinetics of benzophenone-3 after oral exposure in male rats. *J Appl Toxicol*. 1995;15:97–102.

    Okereke CS, Abdel-Rahman MS, Friedman MA. Disposition of benzophenone-3 after dermal administration in male rats. *Toxicol Lett*. 1994;73:113–122.

41. Fediuk DJ, Wang T, Raizman JE, Parkinson FE, GU X. Tissue deposition of the insect repellent DEET and the sunscreen oxybenzone from repeated topical skin applications in rats. *Int J Toxicol*. 2010;29:594–603.

42. Janjua NR, Mogensen B, Andersson AM, et al. Systemic absorption of the sunscreens benzophenone- 3, octyl-methoxycinnamate, and 3-(4-methyl-benzylidene) camphor after whole- body topical application and reproductive hormone levels in humans. *J Invest Dermatol*. 2004;123:57–61.

43. Janjua NR, Kongshoj B, Andersson AM, Wulf HC. Sunscreens in human plasma and urine after repeated whole-body topical application. *J Eur Acad Dermatol Venereol*. 2008;22:456–461.

44. Kadry AM, Okereke CS, Abdel-Rahman MS, Friedman MA, Davis RA. Pharmacokinetics of benzophenone-3 after oral exposure in male rats. *J Appl Toxicol*. 1995;15:97–102.

45. Okereke CS, Abdel-Rhaman MS, Friedman MA. Disposition of benzophenone-3 after dermal administration in male rats. *Toxicol Lett*. 1994;73(2):113-122.

46. Fediuk DJ, Wang T, Raizman JE, Parkinson FE, Gu X. Tissue deposition of the insect repellent DEET and the sunscreen oxybenzone from repeated topical skin applications in rats. *Int J Toxicol.* 2010:29:594–603.

47. Jeon HK, Sarma SN, Kim YJ, Ryu JC. Toxicokinetics and metabolisms of benzophenone-type UV filters in rats. *Toxicology.* 2008 Jun 27;248(2-3):89-95.

48. Janjua NR, Mogensen B, Andersson AM, et al. Systemic absorption of the sunscreens benzophenone-3, octyl-methoxycinnamate, and 3-(4-methyl-benzylidene) camphor after whole-body topical application and reproductive hormone levels in humans. *J Invest Dermatol.* 2004;123:57–61.

49. Krause M, Frederiksen H, Sundberg K, et al. Presence of benzo-phenones commonly used as UV filters and absorbers in paired maternal and fetal samples. *Environ Int.* 2018;110:51-60.

50. Krause M, Klit A, Blomberg Jensen M, Søeborg T, Frederiksen H, Schlumpf M, Lichtensteiger W, Skakkebaek NE, Drzewiecki KT. Sunscreens: are they beneficial for health? An overview of endocrine disrupting properties of UV-filters. *Int J Androl.* 2012 Jun;35(3):424-436.

51. Kajta M, Wójtowicz AK. Impact of endocrine-disrupting chemicals on neural development and the onset of neurological disorders. *Pharmacol Rep.* 2013;65:1632–1639.

52. Gao L, Yuan T, Zhou C, et al. Effects of four commonly used UV filters on the growth, cell viability and oxidative stress responses of the Tetrahymena thermophila. *Chemosphere.* 2013;93:2507–2513.

53. Chen, S.S. Mao, Titanium dioxide nanomaterials: synthesis, properties, modifications, and applications. *Chem Rev.* 2007;107:2891–2959.

    Skocaj M, FilipicM, Petkovi J. Novak S, Titanium dioxide in our everyday life; is it safe? *Radiol Oncol.* 2011;45: 227–247.

54. Karlsson, H.L.; Gustafsson, J.; Cronholm, P.; Moller, L. Size-dependent toxicity of metal oxide particles–A comparison between nano- and micrometer size. *Toxicol Lett.* 2009;188:112–118.

    Sycheva LP, Zhurkov VS, Iurchenko VV, et al. Investigation of genotoxic and cytotoxic effects of micro- and nanosized titanium dioxide in six organs of mice in vivo. *Mutat Res.* 2011;726(1):8-14.

55. Karlsson HL, Gustafsson J, Cronholm P, Möller L. Size-dependent toxicity of metal oxide particles--a comparison between nano- and micrometer size. *Toxicol Lett*. 2009 Jul 24;188(2):112-118.

56. Coccini T, Grandi S, Lonati D, Locatelli C, DE Simone U. Comparative cellular toxicity of titanium dioxide nanoparticles on human astrocyte and neuronal cells after acute and prolonged exposure. *Neurotoxicology*. 2015;48:77–89.

57. Smijs TG, S. Pavel S. Titanium dioxide and zinc oxide nanoparticles in sunscreens: focus on their safety and effectiveness. *Nanotechnol Sci Appl*. 2011;4:95–112.

58. Lu PJ, Cheng WL, Huang SC, Chen YP, Chou HK, Cheng HF. Characterizing titanium dioxide and zinc oxide nanoparticles in sunscreen spray. *Int J Cosmet Sci*. 2015 Dec;37(6):620-626.

59. Buzea C, Pacheco II, Robbie K. Nanomaterials and nanoparticles: sources and toxicity. *Biointerphases*. 2007;2(4):MR17-71.

60. Schilling K, Bradford B, Castelli D, et al. Human safety review of "nano" titanium dioxide and zinc oxide. *Photochem Photobiol Sci*. 2010 Apr;9(4):495-509.

    UC Berkeley News Website. Press Release: DDT in moms harmful to kids, study suggests. Available at: www.berkeley.edu/news/media/releases/2006/07/05_ddt.shtml. Retrieved August 27, 2018.

    Pesticide Action Network Website. The DDT Story. Available at: www.panna.org/resources/ddt-story. Retrieved August 27, 2018.

61. Cohn BA, La Merrill M, Krigbaum NY, et al. DDT Exposure in Utero and Breast Cancer. *J Clin Endocrinol Metab*. 2015 Aug;100(8):2865-2872.

    Warner M, Wesselink A, Harley KG, Bradman A, Kogut K, Eskenazi B. Prenatal exposure to dichlo-rodiphenyltrichloroethane and obesity at 9 years of age in the CHAMACOS study cohort. *Am J Epidemiol*. 2014 Jun 1;179(11):1312-1322.

    Eskenazi B, Mards AR, Bradman A, et al. In utero exposure to dichlorodiphenyltrichloroethane (DDT) and dichlorodiphenyldichloroethylene (DDE) and neurodevelopment among young Mexican American children. *Pediatrics*. 2006;118(1):233-241.

62. Shrivastava R, Raza S, Yadav A, Kushwaha P, Flora SJS. Effects of sub-acute exposure to TiO2 ZnO and Al2O3 nanoparticles on oxidative stress and histological changes in mouse liver and brain. *Drug Chem Toxicol*. 2014;37:336–347.

63. Wu J, Liu W, Xue C, et al. Toxicity and penetration of TiO2 nanoparticles in hairless mice and porcine skin after subchronic dermal exposure. *Toxicol Lett*. 2009;191(1):1-8.

64. Horie M, Sugino S, Kato H, Tabei Y, Nakamura A, Yoshida Y. Does photocatalytic activity of TiO2 nanoparticles correspond to photo-cytotoxicity? Cellular uptake of TiO2 nanoparticles is important in their photo-cytotoxicity. *Toxicol Mech Methods*. 2016;26(4):284-294.

65. Guichard Y, Schmit J, Darne C, et al. Cytotoxicity and genotoxicity of nanosized and microsized titanium dioxide and iron oxide particles in Syrian hamster embryo cells. *Ann Occup Hyg*. 2012;56(5):631-644.

66. European Commision Website. Scientific Committess. Available at: http://ec.europa.eu/health/scientific_committees/experts/declarations/sccs_en.htm. Retrieved May 16, 2018.

67. Gulson B, Mccall M, Korsch M, et al. Small amounts of zinc from zinc oxide particles in sunscreens applied out-doors are absorbed through human skin. *Toxicol Sci*. 2010;118:140–149.

68. Raphael AP, Sundh D, Grice JE, Roberts MS, Soyer HP, Prow TW. Zinc oxide nanoparticle re-moval from wounded human skin. *Nanomedicine* (Lond). 2013;8:1751–1761.

69. Mortensen LJ, Oberdörster G, Pentland AP, Delouise LA. In vivo skin penetration of quantum dot nanoparticles in the murine model: the effect of UVR. *Nano Lett*. 2008 Sep;8(9):2779-2787.

70. Baky NA, Faddah LM, Al-Rasheed NM, Al-Rasheed NM, Fatani AJ. Induction of inflammation, DNA damage and apoptosis in rat heart after oral exposure to zinc oxide nanoparticles and the cardioprotective role of α-lipoic acid and vitamin E. *Drug Res* (Stuttg). 2013;63(5):228-236.

71. Okada Y1, Tachibana K, Yanagita S, Takeda K. Prenatal exposure to zinc oxide particles alters monoaminergic neurotransmitter levels in the brain of mouse offspring. *J Toxicol Sci*. 2013;38:363–370.

71a. Science Daily Website. Keele University. "Aluminum Found In Sunscreen: Could It Cause Skin Cancer? 13 August 2007. Available at: www.sciencedaily.com/releases/2007/08/070812084458. htm. Retrieved November 1, 2018.

71b. Labille J, Feng J, Botta C, Borschneck D, Sammut M, Cabie M, Auffan M, Rose J, Bottero JY. Aging of TiO(2) nanocomposites used in sunscreen. Dispersion and fate of the degradation products in aqueous environment. *Environ Pollut.* 2010;158(12):3482-3489.

71c. Inan-Eroglu E, Ayaz A. Is aluminum exposure a risk factor for neurological disorders? *J Red Med Sci.* 2018; 23:51.

72. Kao YY, Cheng TJ, Yang DM, Wang CT, Chiung YM, Liu PS. Demonstration of an olfactory bulb-brain translocation pathway for ZnO nanoparticles in rodent cells in vitro and in vivo. *J Mol Neuro-sci. 2012;*48:464–471.

73. Pujalté I, Dieme D, Haddad S, Serventi AM, Bouchard M. Toxicokinetics of titanium dioxide (TiO2) nanoparticles after inhalation in rats. *Toxicol Lett.* 2017;265:77-85.

74. French JE. NTP technical report on the toxicity studies of 2-Hydroxy-4-methoxybenzophenone (CAS No. 131-57-7) Administered Topically and in Dosed Feed to F344/N Rats and B6C3F1 Mice. *Toxic Rep Ser.* 1992;21:1-E14.

75. French JE. NTP technical report on the toxicity studies of 2-Hydroxy-4-methoxybenzophenone (CAS No. 131-57-7) Administered Topically and in Dosed Feed to F344/N Rats and B6C3F1 Mice. *Toxic Rep Ser.* 1992;21:1-E14. Available at: https:// ntp.niehs.nih.gov/ntp/htdocs/st_rpts/tox021.pdf. Retrieved June 23, 2018.

76. Schlumpf M, Durrer S, Faass O, et. al. Developmental toxicity of UV filters and environmental exposure: a review. *Int J Androl.* 2008;31(2):144-151.

Durrer S, Ehnes C, Fuetsch M, Maerkel K, Schlumpf M, Lichtensteiger W. Estrogen Sensitivity of Target Genes and Expression of Nuclear Receptor Co-Regulators in Rat Prostate after Pre- and Postnatal Exposure to the Ultraviolet Filter 4-Methylbenzylidene Camphor. *Environ Health Perspect.* 2007; 115(Suppl 1):42–50.

Balmer ME, Buser HR, Müller MD, Poiger T. Occurrence of some organic UV filters in wastewater, in surface waters, and in fish from Swiss Lakes. *Environ Sci Technol.* 2005 Feb 15;39(4):953-962.

Krause M, Klit A, Blomberg Jensen M, Søeborg T, Frederiksen H, Schlumpf M, Lichtensteiger W, Skakkebaek NE, Drzewiecki KT. Sunscreens: are they beneficial for health? An overview of endocrine dis-rupting properties of UV-filters. *Int J Androl.* 2012;35(3):424-436.

Wang J, Pan L, Wu S, et al. Recent advances on endocrine disrupting effects of UV filters. *Int J Environ Res Public Health.* 2016;13(8):782.

77. Krause M, Klit A, Blomberg Jensen M, et al. Sunscreens: are they beneficial for health? An overview of endocrine disrupting properties of UV-filters. *Int J Androl.* 2012 Jun;35(3):424-436.

Schlumpf M, Cotton B, Conscience M, Haller V, Steinmann B, Lichtensteiger W. In vitro and in vivo estrogenicity of UV screens. *Environ Health Perspect.* 2001;109:239–244.

DiNardo JC, Downs CA. Dermatological and environmental toxicological impact of the sunscreening ingredient oxybenzone/benzophenone-3. *J Cosmet Dermal.* 2018;17(1):15-19.

78. Jo E, Seo G, Kwon JT, et al. Exposure to zinc oxide nanoparticles affects reproductive development and biodistribution in offspring rats. *J Toxicol Sci.* 2013;38(4):525-530.

79. Hong F, Si W, Zhao X, et al. TiO2 Nanoparticle Exposure Decreases Spermatogenesis via Biochemical Dysfunctions in the Testis of Male Mice. *J Agric Food Chem.* 2015 Aug 12;63(31):7084-7092.

80. Liu J, Zhao Y, Ge W, et al. Oocyte exposure to ZnO nanoparticles inhibits early embryonic development through the γ-H2AX and NF-κB signaling pathways. *Oncotarget.* 2017; 8:42673–42692.

81. Brohi RD, Wang L, Talpur HS, et al. Toxicity of Nanoparticles on the Reproductive System in Animal Models: A Review. *Front Pharmacol.* 2017 Sep 5;8:606.

Di Virgilio AL, Reigosa M, Arnal PM, Fernández Lorenzo de Mele M. Comparative study of the cytotoxic and genotoxic effects of titanium oxide and aluminium oxide nanoparticles in Chinese hamster ovary (CHO-K1) cells. *J Hazard Mater.* 2010;177:711–718.

Shimizu M, Tainaka H, Oba T, Mizuo K, Umezawa M, Takeda K. Maternal exposure to nanopar-ticulate titanium dioxide during the prenatal period alters gene expression related to brain development in the mouse. *Part Fibre Toxicol.* 2009;6:20.

Mohammadipour A, Fazel A, Haghir H, et al. Maternal exposure to titanium dioxide nanoparticles during pregnancy; impaired memory and decreased hippocampal cell proliferation in rat offspring. *Environ Toxicol Pharmacol*. 2014;37:617–625.

Mohammadipour A, Hosseini M, Fazel A, et al. The effects of exposure to titanium dioxide nanoparticles during lactation period on learning and memory of rat offspring. *Toxicol Ind Health*. 2016;32:221–228.

Umezawa M, Tainaka H, Kawashima N, Shimizu M, Takeda K. Effect of fetal exposure to titanium dioxide nanoparticle on brain development - brain region information. *J Toxicol Sci*. 2012;37:1247–1252.

Yamashita K, Yoshioka Y, Higashisaka K, et al. Silica and titanium dioxide nanoparticles cause preg-nancy complications in mice. *Nat Nanotechnol*. 2011;6:321–328.

Liu J, Zhao Y, Ge W, et al. Oocyte exposure to ZnO nanoparticles inhibits early embryonic development through the γ-H2AX and NF-κB signaling pathways. *Oncotarget*. 2017;8:42673–42692.

82. Gao G, Ze Y, Zhao X, et al. Titanium dioxide nanoparticle-induced testicular damage, spermatogenesis suppression, and gene expression alterations in male mice. *J Hazard Mater*. 2013 Aug 15;258-259:133-143.

83. Khorsandi L, Orazizadeh M, Moradi-Gharibvand N, Hemadi M, Mansouri E. Beneficial effects of quercetin on titanium dioxide nanoparticles induced spermatogenesis defects in mice. *Environ Sci Pollut Res Int*. 2017 Feb;24(6):5595-5606.

84. Yin C, Zhao W, Liu R, et al. TiO2 particles in seafood and surimi products: Attention should be paid to their exposure and uptake through foods. *Chemosphere*. 2017 Dec;188:541-547.

85. Philippat C, Mortamais M, Chevrier C, et al. Exposure to phthalates and phenols during pregnancy and offspring size at birth, *Environ Health Perspect*. 2012;120:464–470.

86. Okada Y1, Tachibana K, Yanagita S, Takeda K. Prenatal exposure to zinc oxide particles alters monoaminergic neurotransmitter levels in the brain of mouse offspring. *J Toxicol Sci*. 2013;38:363–370.

87. Hashemi E, Ariza J, Rogers H, Noctor SC, Martínez-Cerdeño V. The Number of Parvalbumin-Expressing Interneurons Is Decreased in the Medial Prefrontal Cortex in Autism. *Cereb Cortex*. 2017 Mar 1;27(3):1931-1943.

Ajram LA, Horder J, Mendez MA, et. al. Shifting brain inhibitory balance and connectivity of the prefrontal cortex of adults with autism spectrum disorder. *Transl Psychiatry*. 2017 May 23;7(5):e1137.

88. Mohammadipour A, Fazel A, Haghir H, et al. Maternal exposure to titanium dioxide nanoparticles during pregnancy; impaired memory and decreased hippocampal cell proliferation in rat offspring. *Environ Toxicol Pharmacol*. 2014;37(2):617–625.

89. Umezawa M, Tainaka H, Kawashima N, Shimizu M, Takeda K. Effect of fetal exposure to titanium dioxide nanoparticle on brain development–brain region information. *J Toxicol Sci*. 2012;37(6):1247–1252.

90. Tetreault NA, Hakeem AY, Jiang S, et al. Microglia in the cerebral cortex in autism. *J Autism Dev Disord*. 2012 Dec;42(12):2569-2584.

91. Takahashi Y, Mizuo K, Shinkai Y, Oshio S, Takeda K. Prenatal exposure to titanium dioxide nanoparticles increases dopamine levels in the prefrontal cotex and neostriatum of mice. *J Toxicol Sci*. 2010;35(5):749–756.

Umezawa M, Tainaka H, Kawashima N, Shimizu M, Takeda K. Effect of fetal exposure to titanium dioxide nanoparticle on brain development–brain region information. *J Toxicol Sci*. 2012;37(6):1247–1252.

92. Cui Y, Chen X, Zhou Z, et al. Prenatal exposure to nanoparticulate titanium dioxide enhances depressive-like behaviors in adult rats. *Chemosphere*. 2014;96:99–104.

Hougaard KS, Jackson P, Jensen KA, Sloth JJ, Loeschner K, Larsen EH, et al. Effects of prenatal exposure to surface-coated nanosized titanium dioxide (UV-Titan). A study in mice. *Part Fibre Toxicol*. 2010. doi:10.1186/ 1743-8977-7-16.

Shimizu M, Tainaka H, Oba T, Mizuo K, Umezawa M, Takeda K. Maternal exposure to nanoparticulate titanium dioxide during the prenatal period alters gene expression related to brain development in the mouse. *Part Fibre Toxicol*. 2009;6:20.

93. Shimizu M, Tainaka H, Oba T, Mizuo K, Umezawa M, Takeda K. Maternal exposure to nanoparticulate titanium dioxide during the prenatal period alters gene expression related to brain development in the mouse. *Part Fibre Toxicol*. 2009;6:20.

94. Mohammadipour A, Fazel A, Haghir H, et al. Maternal exposure to titanium dioxide nanoparticles during pregnancy; impaired memory and decreased hippocampal cell proliferation in rat offspring. *Environ Toxicol Pharmacol*. 2014;37:617–625.

95. Yamashita K, Yoshioka Y, Higashisaka K, et al. Silica and titanium dioxide nanoparticles cause pregnancy complications in mice. *Nat Nanotechnol*. 2011;6:321–328.

96. Zhang L, Xie X, Zhou Y, et al. Gestational exposure to titanium dioxide nanoparticles impairs the placentation through dysregulation of vascularization, proliferation and apoptosis in mice. *Int J Nanomedicine*. 2018 Feb 5;13:777-789.

97. Shimizu M, Tainaka H, Oba T, Mizuo K, Umezawa M, Takeda K. Maternal exposure to nanoparticulate titanium dioxide during the prenatal period alters gene expression related to brain development in the mouse. *Part Fibre Toxicol*. 2009;6:20.

98. Xu G, Umezawa M, Takeda K: Early development origins of adult disease caused by malnutrition and environmental chemical substances. *J Health Sci*. 2009;55:11-19.

99. Shimizu M, Tainaka H, Oba T, Mizuo K, Umezawa M, Takeda K. Maternal exposure to nanoparticulate titanium dioxide during the prenatal period alters gene expression related to brain development in the mouse. *Part Fibre Toxicol*. 2009;6:20.

100. Ponzo OJ, Silvia C. Evidence of reproductive disruption associated with neuroendocrine changes induced by UV-B filters, phthalates and nonylphenol during sexual maturation in rats of both gender. *Toxicology*. 2013;311:41–51.

    Vela-Soria F, Jiménez-Díaz I, Rodríguez-Gómez R, et al. Determination of benzophenones in human placental tissue samples by liquid chromatography-tandem mass spectrometry. *Talanta*. 2011 Sep 30;85(4):1848-1855.

101. Inui M, Adachi T, Takenaka S, et al. Effect of UV screens and preservatives on vitellogenin and choriogenin production in male medaka (Oryzias latipes). *Toxicology*. 2003 Dec 15;194(1-2):43-50.

102. Jarry H, Christoffel J, Rimoldi G, Koch L, Wuttke W. Multi-organic endocrine disrupting activity of the UV screen benzophenone 2 (BP2) in ovariectomized adult rats after 5 days treatment. *Toxicology.* 2004 Dec 1;205(1-2):87-93.

103. Schreurs Rh, Sonneveld E, JansenJH, Seinen W, van der Burg B. Interaction of polycyclic musks and UV Filters with the estrogen receptor (ER), androgen receptor (AR), and progesterone receptor (PR) in reporter gene bioassays. *Toxicol Sci.* 2004;83:264–272.

104. Molina-Molina JM, Escande A, Pillon A, et al. Profiling of benzophenone derivatives using fish and human estrogen receptor-specific in vitro bioassays. *Toxicol Appl Pharmacol.* 2008;232:384–395.

105. Zucchi S, Blüthgen N, Ieronimo A, Fent K. The UV-absorber benzophenone-4 alters transcripts of genes involved in hormonal pathways in zebrafish (Danio rerio) eleuthero-embryos and adult males. *Toxicol Appl Pharmacol.* 2011;250:137–146.

106. Durrer S, Ehnes C, Fuetsch M, Maerkel K, Schlumpf M, Lichtensteiger W. Estrogen sensitivity of target genes and expression of nuclear receptor co-regulators in rat prostate after pre- and postnatal exposure to the ultraviolet filter 4-methylbenzylidene camphor. *Environ Health Perspect.* 2007 Dec; 115(Suppl 1):42–50.

107. Negri-Cesi P, Colciago A, Celotti F, Motta M. Sexual differentiation of the brain: role of testosterone and its active metabolites. *J Endocrinol Invest.* 2004;27(6 Suppl):120-127.

108. Scinicariello F, Buser MC. Serum Testosterone Concentrations and Urinary Bisphenol A, Benzophenone-3, triclosan, and paraben levels in male and female children and adolescents: NHANES 2011-2012. *Environ Health Perspect.* 2016 Dec;124(12):1898-1904.

109. Jeon HK, Sarma SN, Kim YJ, Ryu JC. Toxicokinetics and metabolisms of benzophenone-type UV filters in rats. *Toxicology.* 2008 Jun 27;248(2-3):89-95.

110. Dunaway S, Odin R, Zhou L, Ji L, Zhang Y, Kadekaro AL. Natural antioxidants: multiple mechanisms to protect skin from solar radiation. *Front Pharmacol.* 2018 Apr 24;9:392.

111. Saptarshi SR, Duschl A, Lopata AL.Biological reactivity of zinc oxide nanoparticles with mammalian test systems: an overview. *Nanomedicine* (Lond). 2015;10(13):2075-2092.

112. Tian L, Lin B, Wu L, et al. Neurotoxicity induced by zinc oxide nano-particles: age-related differences and interaction. *Sci Rep.* 2015;5:16117.

113. Baky NA, Faddah LM, Al-Rasheed NM, Al-Rasheed NM, Fatani AJ. Induction of inflammation, DNA damage and apoptosis in rat heart after oral exposure to zinc oxide nanoparticles and the cardioprotective role of α-lipoic acid and vitamin E. *Drug Res* (Stuttg). 2013 May;63(5):228-236.

114. Savi M, Rossi S, Bocchi L, et al. Titanium dioxide nanoparticles promote arrhythmias via a direct interaction with rat cardiac tissue. *Part Fibre Toxicol.* 2014 Dec 9;11:63.

115. Johnson BM, Fraietta JA, Gracias DT, et al. Acute exposure to ZnO nanoparticles induces autophagic immune cell death. *Nanotoxicology.* 2015;9(6):737-748.

116. Sruthi S, Mohanan PV. Engineered Zinc Oxide Nanoparticles; Biological Interactions at the Organ Level. *Curr Med Chem.* 2016;23(35):4057-4068.

117. Jarry H, Christoffel J, Rimoldi G, Koch L, Wuttke W. Multi-organic endocrine disrupting activity of the UV screen benzophenone 2 (BP2) in ovariectomized adult rats after 5 days treatment. *Toxicology.* 2004 Dec 1;205(1-2):87-93.

118. Klammer H, Schlecht C, Wuttke W, et al. Effects of a 5-day treatment with the UV-filter octyl-methoxycinnamate (OMC) on the function of the hypothalamo-pituitary-thyroid function in rats. *Toxicology.* 2007 Sep 5;238(2-3):192-199.

119. Axelstad M, Boberg J, Hougaard KS, et al. Effects of pre- and postnatal exposure to the UV-filter octyl methoxycinnamate (OMC) on the reproductive, auditory and neurological development of rat offspring. *Toxicol Appl Pharmacol.* 2011 Feb 1;250(3):278-290.

120. Krause M, Klit A, Blomberg Jensen M, et al. Sunscreens: are they beneficial for health? An overview of endocrine disrupting properties of UV-filters. *Int J Androl.* 2012 Jun;35(3):424-436.
     Schlumpf M, Cotton B, Conscience M, Haller V, Steinmann B, Lichtensteiger W. In vitro and in vivo estrogenicity of UV screens. *Environ Health Perspect.* 2001;109:239–244.

121. Lecomte S, Habauzit D, Charlier TD, Pakdel F. Emerging estrogenic pollutants in the aquatic environment and breast cancer. *Genes* (Basel). 2017 Sep 15;8(9). pii: E229.

122. Alamer M, Darbre PD. Effects of exposure to six chemical ultraviolet filters commonly used in personal care products on motility of MCF-7 and MDA-MB-231 human breast cancer cells in vitro. *J Appl Toxicol.* 2018 Feb;38(2):148-159.

123. Prins GS. Endocrine disruptors and prostate cancer risk. *Endocr Relat Cancer.* 2008 Sep;15(3):649-656.

124. Mohr SB, Gorham ED, Garland CF, Grant WB, Garland FC, Cuomo RE. Are low ultraviolet B and vitamin D associated with higher incidence of multiple myeloma? *J Steroid Biochem Mol Biol.* 2015 Apr;148:245-252.

125. Pietroiusti A, Bergamaschi E, Campagna M, et al. The unrecognized occupational relevance of the interaction between engineered nanomaterials and the gastrointestinal tract: a consensus paper from a multidisciplinary working group. *Part Fibre Toxicol.* 2017 Nov 25;14(1):47.

126. Filippi C, Pryde A, Cowan P, et al. Toxicology of ZnO and TiO2 nanoparticles on hepatocytes: impact on metabolism and bioenergetics. *Nanotoxicology.* 2015 Feb;9(1):126-134.

127. Guo D, Bi H, Wang Q. WU, Zinc oxide nanoparticles decrease the expression and activity of plasma membrane calcium ATPase, disrupt the intracellular calcium homeostasis in rat retinal ganglion cells. *Int J Biochem Cell Biol.* 2013;45:1849–1859.

128. Wang J, Deng X, Zhang F, Chen D, Ding W. ZnO nanoparticle-induced oxidative stress triggers apoptosis by activating JNK signaling pathway in cultured primary astrocytes. *Nanoscale Res. Lett.* 2014 Mar 13;9(1):11.

128a. Nicolson GL. Mitochondrial dysfunction and chronic disease: treatment with natural aupplements. *Integr Med* (Encinitas). 2014;13(4):35–43.

129. Mohr SB, Garland CF, Gorham ED, Garland FC. The association between ultraviolet B irradiance, vitamin D status and incidence rates of type 1 diabetes in 51 regions worldwide. *Diabetologia.* 2008 Aug;51(8):1391-1398.

130. Filippi C, Pryde A, Cowan P, et al. Toxicology of ZnO and TiO2 nanoparticles on hepatocytes: impact on metabolism and bioenergetics. *Nanotoxicology.* 2015 Feb;9(1):126-134.

131. Heller A, Jarvis K, Coffman SS. Association of type 2 diabetes with submicron titanium dioxide crystals in the pancreas. *Chem Res Toxicol.* 2018 Jun 18;31(6):506-509.

132. Li Y, Li J, Yin J, et al. Systematic influence induced by 3 nm titanium dioxide following intratracheal instillation of mice. *J Nanosci Nanotechnol.* 2010 Dec;10(12):8544-8549.

133. Domínguez A, Suárez-Merino B, Goñi-de-Cerio F. Nanoparticles and blood-brain barrier: the key to central nervous system diseases. *J Nanosci Nanotechnol.* 2014 Jan;14(1):766-779.

134. Disdier C, Chalansonnet M, Gagnaire F, et al. Brain inflammation, blood brain barrier dysfunction and neuronal synaptophysin decrease after inhalation exposure to titanium dioxide nano-aerosol in aging rats. *Sci Rep.* 2017 Sep 22;7(1):12196.

135. Bird CM, Burgess N. The hippocampus and memory: insights from spatial processing. *Nat Rev Neurosci.* 2008;9(3):182–194.

      Howland JG, Wang YT. Synaptic plasticity in learning and memory: stress effects in the hippocampus. *Prog Brain Res.* 2008;169:145–158.

      Ashbrook DG, Williams RW, Lu L, et al. Joint genetic analysis of hippocampal size in mouse and human identifies a novel gene linked to neurodegenerative disease. *BMC Genomics.* 2014 Oct 3;15:850.

      Ceccariglia S, D'Altocolle A, Del Fa A, et al. Increased expression of aquaporin 4 in the Rat hippocampus and cortex during trimethyltin-induced neurodegeneration. *Neuroscience.* 2014;274:273–288.

      Lin TW, Shih YH, Chen SJ, et al. Running exercise delays neurodegeneration in amygdala and hippocampus of Alzheimer's disease (APP/PS1) transgenic mice. *Neurobiol Learn Mem.* 2015;118:189–197.

136. Woodward MR, Amrutkar CV, Shah HC, et al. Validation of olfactory deficit as a biomarker of Alzheimer disease. *Neurol Clin Pract.* 2017 Feb;7(1):5-14.

137. Zhao J, Xu L, Zhang T, Ren G, Yang Z. Influences of nanoparticle zinc oxide on acutely isolated rat hippocampal CA3 pyramidal neurons. *Neurotoxicology.* 2009;30:220–230.

138. Migliore L, Uboldi C, Di Bucchianico S, Coppedè F. Nanomaterials and neurodegeneration. *Environ Mol Mutagen.* 2015;56:149–170.

139. Coccini T, Grandi S, Lonati D, Locatelli C, DE Simone U. Comparative cellular toxicity of titanium dioxide nanoparticles on human astrocyte and neuronal cells after acute and prolonged exposure. *Neurotoxicology.* 2015;48:77–89.

140. Liu S, XU L, Zhang T, Ren G, Yang Z. Oxidative stress and apoptosis induced by nanosized titanium dioxide in PC12 cells. *Toxicology*. 2010;267:172–177.

141. Okada Y, Tachibana K, Yanagita S, Takeda K. Prenatal exposure to zinc oxide particles alters monoaminergic neurotransmitter levels in the brain of mouse offspring. *J Toxicol Sci*. 2013;38:363–370.

142. Cui Y, Chen X, Zhou Z, et al. Prenatal exposure to nanoparticulate titanium dioxide enhances depressive-like behaviors in adult rats. *Chemosphere*. 2014;96:99–104.

143. Blüthgen N, Meili N, Chew G, Odermatt A, Fent K. Accumulation and effects of the UV-filter octocrylene in adult and embryonic zebrafish (Danio rerio). *Sci Total Environ*. 2014 Apr 1;476-477:207-217.

144. Wang MM, Wang YC, Wang XN, et al. Mutagenicity of ZnO nanoparticles in mammalian cells: Role of physicochemical transformations under the aging process. *Nanotoxicology*. 2015;9(8):972-982.

145. Chiang HM, Xia Q, Zou X, et al. Nanoscale ZnO induces cytotoxicity and DNA damage in human cell lines and rat primary neuronal cells. *J Nanosci Nanotechnol*. 2012;12:2126–2135.

146. Pati R, Das I, Mehta RK, Sahu R, Sonawane A. Zinc-oxide nanoparticles exhibit genotoxic, clastogenic, cytotoxic and actin depolymerization effects by inducing oxidative stress responses in macrophages and adult mice. *Toxicol Sci*. 2016 Apr;150(2):454-472.

   Singh N, Nelson BC, Scanlan LD , Coskun E, Jaruga P, Doak SH. Exposure to engineered nanomaterials: impact on DNA repair pathways. *Int J Mol Sci*. 2017 Jul 13;18(7). pii: E1515.

147. Moffitt & Caspi Website. Gene X Environment. Available at: https://moffittcaspi.com/content/gene-x-environment. Retrieved November 25, 2017.

148. Patil NA, Gade WN, Deobagkar DD. Epigenetic modulation upon exposure of lung fibroblasts to TiO2 and ZnO nanoparticles: alterations in DNA methylation. *Int J Nanomedicine*. 2016 Sep 7;11:4509-4519.

149. Sierra MI, Valdés A, Fernández AF, Torrecillas R, Fraga MF. The effect of exposure to nanoparticles and nanomaterials on the mammalian epigenome. *Int J Nanomedicine*. 2016 Nov 25;11:6297-6306.

150. Lu X, Miousse IR, Pirela SV, Melnyk S, Koturbash I, Demokritou P. Short-term exposure to engineered nanomaterials affects cellular epigenome. *Nanotoxicology*. 2016;10(2):140-150.

151. Scherzad A, Meyer T, Kleinsasser N, Hackenberg S. Molecular mechanisms of zinc oxide nanoparticle-induced genotoxicity short running title: Genotoxicity of ZnO NPs. *Materials* (Basel). 2017 Dec 14;10(12). pii: E1427.

152. Patil NA, Gade WN, Deobagkar DD. Epigenetic modulation upon exposure of lung fibroblasts to TiO2 and ZnO nanoparticles: alterations in DNA methylation. *Int J Nanomedicine*. 2016 Sep 7;11:4509-4519.
Sharma S, Kelly TK, Peter A. Jones PA. Epigenetics in cancer. *Carcinogenesis*. 2010 Jan;31(1):27–36.

153. Wnuk A, Rzemieniec J, Lason W, Krzeptowski W, Kajta M. Benzophenone-3 impairs autophagy, alters epigenetic status, and disrupts Retinoid X receptor signaling in apoptotic neuronal cells. *Mol Neurobiol*. 2018;55(6):5059–5074.

154. Sharifan H, Klein D, Morse AN. UV filters interaction in the chlorinated swimming pool, a new challenge for urbanization, a need for community scale investigations. *Environ Res*. 2016;148:273–276.

155. Ramos S, Homem V, Alves A, Santos L. Advances in analytical methods and occurrence of organic UV-filters in the environment–A review. *Sci Total Environ*. 2015;526:278–311.

156. Sherwood VF, Kennedy S, Zhang H, Purser GH, Sheaff RJ. Altered UV absorbance and cytotoxicity of chlorinated sunscreen agents. *Cutan Ocul Toxicol*. 2012 Dec;31(4):273-279.

157. Sharifan H, Klein D, Morse AN. UV filters interaction in the chlorinated swimming pool, a new challenge for urbanization, a need for community scale investigations. *Environ Res*. 2016 Jul;148:273-276.

158. Makarova A, Wang G, Dolorito JA, Kc S, Libove E, Epstein EH Jr. Vitamin D3 produced by skin exposure to UVR inhibits murine basal cell carcinoma carcinogenesis. *J Invest Dermatol*. 2017 Dec;137(12):2613-2619.

159. Baggerly CA, Cuomo RE, French CB, et al. Sunlight and vitamin D: Necessary for public health. *J Am Coll Nutr*. 2015;34(4):359-365.

160. Park SK, Garland CF, Gorham ED, BuDoff L, Barrett-Connor E. Plasma 25-hydroxyvitamin D concentration and risk of type 2 diabetes and pre-diabetes: 12-year cohort study. *PLoS One.* 2018 Apr 19;13(4):e0193070.

161. Ren X, Zhao X, Duan X, Fang Z. Enhanced bio-concentration of tris(1,3-dichloro-2-propyl) phosphate in the presence of nano-TiO2 can lead to adverse reproductive outcomes in zebrafish. *Environ Pollut.* 2018 Feb;233:612-622.

162. KQED Website. Standen A. It's Official: Toxic Flame Retardants No Longer Required in Furniture. Available at: www.kqed. org/science/11318/its-official-toxic-flame-retardants-no-longer-required-in-furniture. Retrieved May 16, 2018.

163. IPCS-CEC (2005). Benzophenone. CAS No. 119–61–9. ICSC (International Chemical Safety Cards): 0389 Peer reviewed 2010. International Programme on Food Safety-Commission of the European Communities. Available at: http://www .inchem. org /documents/icsc/icsc/eics0389.html. [Reference list]. As cited in IARC Monographs on the Evaluation of Carcinogenic Risks to Humans, No. 101. *IARC Working Group on the Evaluation of Carcinogenic Risk to Humans.* Lyon (FR): International Agency for Research on Cancer; 2013. Available at: www.ncbi.nlm.nih. gov/books/NBK373188/. Retrieved: October 30, 2018.

Parks N. UV-stabilizing chemicals contaminating Japan's marine environment. *Environ Sci Technol.* 2009;43:6896–6897. PMID:19806714. [PubMed] [Reference list]. As cited in IARC Monographs on the Evaluation of Carcinogenic Risks to Humans, No. 101. *IARC Working Group on the Evaluation of Carcinogenic Risk to Humans.* Lyon (FR): International Agency for Research on Cancer; 2013. Available at: www.ncbi.nlm.nih. gov/books/NBK373188/. Retrieved: October 30, 2018.

164. Ramos S, Homem V, Alves A, Santos L. Advances in analytical methods and occurrence of organic UV-filters in the environment–A review. *Sci Total Environ.* 2015;526:278–311.

Kim S, Choi K. Occurrences, toxicities, and ecological risks of benzophenone-3, a common component of organic sunscreen products: a mini-review. *Environ Int.* 2014;70:143–157.

Sanchez-Quiles D, Tovar-Sanchez Z. Are sunscreens a new environmental risk associated with coastal tourism? *Environ Int.* 2015;83:158–170.

165. Tovar-Sánchez A, Sánchez-Quiles D, Basterretxea G, et al. Sunscreen products as emerging pollutants to coastal waters, *PLoS One.* 2013;8:e65451.

166. Kim S, Choi K2. Occurrences, toxicities, and ecological risks of benzophenone-3, a common component of organic sunscreen products: a mini-review. *Environ Int.* 2014 Sep;70:14357.

    Watanabe Y, Kojima H, Takeuchi S, et al. Metabolism of UV-filter benzophenone-3 by rat and human liver microsomes and its effect on endocrine-disrupting activity. *Toxicol Appl Pharmacol.* 2015 Jan 15;282(2):119-128.

167. Fent K, Zenker A, Rapp M. Widespread occurrence of estrogenic UV-filters in aquatic ecosystems in Switzerland. *Environ Pollut.* 210;158:1817–1824.

168. Fent K, Kunz PY, Gomez E. UV filters in the aquatic environment induce hormonal effects and affect fertility and reproduction in fish. Endocrine disruptors: natural waters and fishes. *Chimia.* 2008;62(5):368-375.

169. Díaz-Cruz MS, Gago-Ferrero P, Llorca M, Barceló D. Analysis of UV filters in tap water and other clean waters in Spain. *Anal Bioanal Chem.* 2012 Mar;402(7):2325-2333..

170. Mizukawa A, Molins-Delgado D, de Azevedo JCR, Fernandes CVS, Díaz-Cruz S, Barceló D. Sediments as a sink for UV filters and benzotriazoles: the case study of Upper Iguaçu watershed, Curitiba (Brazil). *Environ Sci Pollut Res Int.* 2017 Aug;24(22):18284-18294.

171. Danovaro R, Bongiorni L, Corinaldesi C, et al. Sunscreens cause coral bleaching by promoting viral infections. *Environ Health Perspect.* 2008;116(4):441-447.

172. Downs CA, Kramarsky-Winter E, Segal R, et. al. Toxicopathological effects of the sunscreen UV filter oxy- benzone (Benzophenone-3), on coral planulae and cultured primary cells and its environmental contamination in Hawaii and the U.S. Virgin Islands. *Arch Environ Contam Toxicol.* 2016;70:265–288.

173. Blüthgen N, Meili N, Chew G, Odermatt A, Fent K. Accumulation and effects of the UV-filter octocrylene in adult and embryonic zebrafish (Danio rerio). *Sci Total Environ.* 2014 Apr 1;476-477:207-217.

174. Fahmy SR, Abdel-Ghaffar F, Bakry FA, Sayed DA. Ecotoxicological effect of sublethal exposure to zinc oxide nanoparticles on freshwater snail Biomphalaria alexandrina. *Arch Environ Contam Toxicol.* 2014 Aug;67(2):192-202.

175. Zhang QY, Ma XY, Wang XC, Ngo HH. Assessment of multiple hormone activities of a UV-filter (octocrylene) in zebrafish (Danio rerio). *Chemosphere.* 2016 Sep;159:433-441.

176. Molins-Delgado D, Máñez M, Andreu A, et al. A potential new threat to wild life: Presence of UV Filters in bird eggs from a preserved area. *Environ Sci Technol.* 2017 Oct 3;51(19):10983-10990.

177. Wu MH, Xie DG, Xu G, et al. Benzophenone-type UV filters in surface waters: An assessment of profiles and ecological risks in Shanghai, China. *Ecotoxicol Environ Saf.* 2017 Jul;141:235-241.

178. Gao L, Yuan T, Zhou C, et al. Effects of four commonly used UV filters on the growth, cell viability and oxidative stress responses of the Tetrahymena thermophila. *Chemosphere.* 2013 Nov;93(10):2507-2513.

179. Miller RJ, Bennett S, Keller AA, Pease S, Lenihan HS. TiO2 nanoparticles are phototoxic to marine phytoplankton. *PLoS One.* 2012;7(1):e30321.

180. Zhu X, Zhu L, Duan Z, Qi R, Li Y, Lang Y. Comparative toxicity of several metal oxide nanoparticle aqueous suspensions to Zebrafish (Danio rerio) early developmental stage. *J Environ Sci Health A Tox Hazard Subst Environ Eng.* 2008 Feb 15;43(3):278-284.

181. Hawaii State Senate Website. S.B No. 2271. Available at: www.capitol.hawaii.gov/session2018/bills/SB2571_.HTM. Retrieved July 15, 2018.

182. Oregon State University Website. Micronutrient information center: Zinc. Available at: http://lpi.oregonstate.edu/infocenter/minerals/zinc/. Retrived December 23, 2010.

Miao AJ, Zhang XY, Luo Z, et al. Zinc oxide-engineered nanoparticles: dissolution and toxicity to marine phytoplankton. *Environ Toxicol Chem.* 2010;29(12):2814-2822.

Answers.com Website. Phytoplankton. Available at: www.answers.com/topic/ phytoplankton. Retrieved November 27, 2010.

NASA Website. What are phytoplankton? Available at: www. earthobservatory. nasa.gov/Features/Phytoplankton/. Retrieved December 22, 2010.

Miller RJ, Lenihan HS, Muller EB, Tseng N, Hanna SK, Keller AA. Impacts of metal oxide nanoparticles on marine phytoplankton. *Environ Sci Technol.* 2010;44(19):7329-7344

Wong SW, Leung PT, Djurisic AB, Leung KM. Toxicities of nano zinc oxide to five marine organisms: influences of aggregate size and ion solubility. *Anal Bioanal Chem.* 2010;396(2):609-618.

Kahru A, Dubourguier HC. From ecotoxicology to nanoecotoxicology. *Toxicology.* 2010;269(2-3):105-119.

183. Chhabra G, Ndiaye MA, Garcia-Peterson LM, Ahmad N. Melanoma Chemoprevention: Current Status and Future Prospects. *Photochem Photobiol.* 2017 Jul;93(4):975-989.

184 Nichols JA, Katiyar SK. Skin photoprotection by natural polyphenols: anti-inflammatory, antioxidant and DNA repair mechanisms. *Arch Dermatol Res.* 2010 Mar;302(2):71-83.

185. Dunaway S, Odin R, Zhou L, Ji L, Zhang Y, Kadekaro AL. Natural antioxidants: Multiple mechanisms to protect skin from solar radiation. *Front Pharmacol.* 2018 Apr 24;9:392.

186. Abu Zeid EH, Alam RTM, Abd El-Hameed NE. Impact of titanium dioxide on androgen receptors, seminal vesicles and thyroid hormones of male rats: possible protective trial with aged garlic extract. *Andrologia.* 2017 Jun;49(5). doi: 10.1111/and.12651.

187. Bissonnette, R. Update on sunscreens. *Skin Therapy Lett.* 2008. 13(6):5-7. Available at: www.medscape.com/viewarticle/582990. Retrieved June 12, 2011.

188. Cancer News in Context Website. Does Sunscreen Prevent Skin Cancers? Available at: www.cancernewsincontext.org/2010/07/ does-sunscreen-prevent-skin-cancer.html. Retrieved January 2, 2011.

Marks R. The changing incidence and mortality of melanoma in Australia. *Recent Results Cancer Res.* 2002;160:113-121.

189. Australian Government: Therapeutic Goods Admin (TGA) Website. Consultation: Australian Regulatory Guidelines for OTC Medicines – Sunscreens. Available at: www.tga.gov. au/npmeds/consult/cons-argom-sunscreens.htm. Document available at: www.tga.gov.au/npmeds/consult/cons-argom-sunscreens.pdf. Retrieved January 26, 2011.

190. Faurschou A, Wulf HC. Ecological analysis of the relation be-tween sunbeds and skin cancer. *Photodermatol Photoimmunol Photomed.* 2007;23(4):120-125.

191. Armas LA, Fusaro RM, Sayre RM, Huerter CJ, Heaney RP. Do melanoidins induced by topical 9% dihydroxyacetone sunless tanning spray inhibit vitamin d production? A pilot study. *Photochem Photobiol.* 2009;85(5):1265-1266.

192. CDC Website. Ansdell VE. Sunburn. Available at: wwwnc.cdc. gov/travel/yellowbook/2010/chapter-2/sunburn.aspx. Retrieved January 24, 2011.

193. Science Daily Website. Nanoparticles Used in Common Household Items Cause Genetic Damage in Mice. Available at: www. sciencedaily.com/releases/2009/11/091116165739.htm. Retrieved February 10, 2011. Interview of co-author of: Trouiller B, Reliene R, Westbrook A, Solaimani P, Schiestl RH. Titanium dioxide nanoparticles induce DNA damage and genetic instability in vivo in mice. *Cancer Res.* 2009;69(22):8784-8789.

194. Matts PJ, Fink B. Chronic sun damage and the perception of age, health and attractiveness. *Photochem Photobiol Sci.* 2010;9(4):421–431.

A

ADHD (attention deficit hyperactivity disorder), 69, 89, 93
after sun protection, 109-110
air pollution, 97
algae, 102-103
allergic reactions, 79, 122
ALS (amyotrophic lateral sclerosis), 81
aluminum, 60
    Alzheimer's, 60
    multiple sclerosis, 60
    neurodevelopmental toxicity, 60
    Parkinson's, 60
aluminum oxide (AL2O3) 57
Alzheimer's, 60, 69, 81-82, 84-85, 90
American, 35, 46-47
amniotic fluid, 48-49
aminobenzoic acid (PABA), 38
amphibians, 39
androgen (male hormone), 46
anthocyanins, 109
antioxidant, food sources, 77, 88, 106-107, 109-110, 113, 125
antioxidants, 31, 44, 86, 109-110, 125
aquatic environment, 39, 44-45, 101, 104-105, 125, 146, 151
aquatic invertebrates, 39
atherosclerosis, 77, 81, 93
Australia, 33, 118,124, 132, 153
    Therapeutic Goods Administration (TGS), 118
    SunSmart Program, 117
autoimmune diseases, 81, 93
autism, 67, 69, 81-82, 89, 93, 113
avobenzone, 38, 43-44

B

basal cell carcinoma, 25, 32-33, 94-95, 121
benzophenones, 31, 38-43, 46-49, 63, 71-72, 76, 79, 101-102, 106
    adhesives, 42
    antihistamines, 42
    companies, 35
    flavor ingredient, 42
    fragrance enhancer, 42
    household cleaners, 42
    hypnotic drugs, 42
    insecticides, 42
    laundry products, 42
    metabolites, 43, 48
    perfume fixative, 42
beta-carotene, 109
beta-endorphins, 95-96
birth defects, 40
birds, 39
bisphenol A (BPA), 72
Black. *See* races, Black
blood, 56
blood-brain barrier, 50, 84, 147
bone (loss), 93-4
BP3, *See* benzophenones
BPA (bisphenol A), 72
brain, 47- 48, 50, 56-8, 60-1, 63-64, 66-69, 72-73, 76, 84-87, 96, 126
    hippocampus, 67
    prefrontal cortex, 67
Brazil, 102
breast cancer, 49, 57, 79-80, 89
    metastatic migration, 79
breast cancer cell line, 79
breast milk, 49, 79, 102
broad-spectrum, 27-28, 118-119
Brown, Jerry, 99

C

calcium, 81, 93-94
California's Bureau of Home
    Furnishings, 99
California's State Legislature's
    Proposition 65, 43-44
camphors, 38, 45-47, 63, 71-72, 79,
    102
cancer, 23-7, 30-33, 40, 43-44, 49-
    50, 57, 72, 75, 79-82, 89,
    91, 95-95, 106, 110, 113,
    117-119, 121, 123, 125
    bladder, 89, 91
    breast, 49, 57, 79-80, 89
    cervical, 89
    colorectum, 89
    esophagus, 89
    intestinal, 91
    liver, 89
    lung, 89
    prostate, 80, 89
    skin, 19, 23-5, 27-34, 49-51, 95,
        106, 110, 117-119, 121
    stomach, 89
    thyroid, 89
Cancer Research, 123
cardiomyocytes, 77
cardiovascular diseases, 77, 81-32
carotenoids, 109
CDC Environment Fact Sheet BP3,
    40
cell,
    cycle, 75,
    death, 44, 53, 64-65, 66-68, 75,
        77, 79, 81, 91, 123
    membrane, 50
central nervous system, 85
chemical filters, 37-50, 79, 101
cholesterol, 24, 104
statin drugs, 107
sulfate, 98

Cindy and Erica's Obsession: To
    Solve America's Health Care
    Crisis, 98
cinnamates, 31, 44, 46-47, 50, 71,
    78-79, 102
Cinoxate, 38
circadian rhythms, 95-96
clothes, 124
coatings, 42
collagen, 58
colon cell lining, 53
conditioners, 41
coral bleaching, 103
coral reefs, 17, 104
cord blood, 48-49
cosmetics (make up), 39, 43, 41, 44-
    46, 65, 104, 123
    companies, 35
Council on Scientific Affairs, 31
crustaceans, 101
cytoplasm, 57
cytotoxicity, 109

D

Danovaro, Roberto, 103
DDE, 57
DDT, 57
DEET, 47
depressive-like behavior, 86
dermatitis (eczema), 93
dermis, 27-30, 97
developmental, 37, 68, 87, 90
    toxicity, 39, 46, 63-64, 66, 98,
        104
diabetes, 81-3, 93-94, 97, 107
diet, 94, 97
Dioxybenzone (benzophenone-8), 38
DNA, 54-56, 59, 64, 68, 75, 85, 106,
    114
    damage, 87-91
dopamine, 57, 66-67, 85

E

Ecamsule, 45
ecological harm, 101-106
embryos, 45, 59, 64, 72, 104-106
endocrine disrupting chemicals
        (EDCs), 51, 53, 72, 78, 80,
        97
environmental pollution, 97
epidemiology, 40
epidermis, 28-30, 44, 97
epinephrine, 85
Escalol 517, 44
esophagus, 53
estrogen/estradiol (female hormone),
        39, 46, 48, 63, 71-73, 78-80,
        98
Europe (an), 34-5, 38, 45-46, 59, 72
    Science Foundation, 89
    union, 59, 79, 116
Eusolex 9020, 44

F

feminization, 39
fetal blood, 48
fetal development, 40, 46, 49, 60, 64,
        66-8, 71-73, 80, 106
fetus, 40, 48-9, 58, 63-9, 71, 86
fish, 39, 66, 71-2, 98-9, 101-102,
        104-105, 125
    intersex, 71
flame (fire) retardant, 39, 98-99
    TiO2, 71
flavonoids, 109
follicle-stimulating hormone (FSH),
        98
Food and Drug Administration
        (FDA), 26-8, 34, 37-38,
        45-47, 50-54, 58-59, 65, 79,
        106, 111, 119
food chain, 101, 105

*Fourth National Report on Human
        Exposure to Environmental
        Chemicals,* 41
Frontiers of Pharmacology, 109

G

gastrointestinal tract, 66
garlic, 110
gender confusion,
        bending (dysphoria), 71-73
gene mutations, 87
global temperature, xvii
    water, xvii
glutathione, 104
Grassroots Health, 95

H

hat, 34
Hawaii, 104, 106
high blood pressure, 93
hippocampus, 67-68, 76, 84
hormone receptor, 38-39, 71
homosalate, 38
human fetus, 48-49, 56, 63-69
hyperactivity disorder (adhd), 69,
        89, 93
hypodermis, 28-30
hypothalamic-pituitary-thyroid
axis (HPT), 39, 63, 78

I

immune system, 39, 75, 77-78, 93,
        102
infertility, 24
inflammation, 32, 54, 63, 67-68, 75-
        8, 84-5, 88
infrared (IR), 29
    IRA, 29-30,
    IRB, 29-30
    IRC, 29-30

International Journal of Environmental Research and Public Health, 34

intestine, 94

J

Journal of Andrology, 49
Journal of Applied Toxicology, 79
Journal of the National Cancer Institute, 32
Journal of Toxicological Sciences, 59

K

kidneys, 46-47, 61, 63-64, 84, 88, 91, 94

L

lakes, 102
latitude, 34, 80, 83
leaky gut, 80-81
learning, 67-68, 76, 84
    disabilities, 82
lotions, 41
liver, 40, 46-7, 54, 57-58, 61, 63-64, 68, 71-72, 77-78, 82-84, 87-89, 91, 94, 107, 122
lungs, 61, 94
lupus, 81
luteinizing hormone (LH), 98
lymphatic (nodes), 56, 61

M

mammals, 39, 89, 101
Material Safety Data Sheets (MSDS), 39-42

medications, 121
Medscape, 117
melanin, 25, 27
melanoma, 23, 25-28, 31-35, 49-50, 106-7, 110, 171, 121
    incidence rate, 25, 117
memory, 39, 67-68, 76, 84-85
menstrual cycles, 45
menthyl anthranilate, 38
metabolic syndrome, 81
methylation, *See* MTHFR
Mexoryl SX, 45
mice, 31, 53, 57-58, 63-68, 76, 84-87
Milestab 1789, 44
mitochondria, 58, 67-69
    dysfunction, 81-82, 90
Molecular Neurobiology, 90
mosquito repellent, 47
MTHFR, 88-90
multiple myeloma, 80
multiple sclerosis, 93
mutagenic industrial chemical compound, 91
mutagenicity, 40

N

nanoparticles (NP), nanomaterials, 24, 26, 34, 51-60, 64-66, 68, 75, 77, 83-85, 88-89, 105-106, 123-124
    blood-brain barrier, 84
    cosmetics, 65-69
    cytoplasm, 57
    nucleus, 51, 56, 66
    titanium dioxide (TiO2), 51-61, 65, 110
    zinc oxide (ZnO), 51-61, 64, 75, 77
nasal, 61

*National Health and Nutrition
   Examination Survey*
   (NHANES), 72
National Toxicology Program (NTP),
   63
near infrared (NIR), 29, 31
Neo Heliopan 357, 44
neurobehavioral, 67, 82
neurotransmitters, 57, 66-68, 85,
   88, 96
neurotoxicity, 40
New Voice for Health Newsletter,
   113
nervous system, 56, 91
nitric oxide, 95-96
norepinephrine, 57, 85
NSAIDs, 107
nucleus, 46, 51, 56, 66, 71

O

obesity, 57, 93, 97-98
obesogens, 97-98
oceans, 101, 105-106, 124-126
   temperature, xvii
octocrylene (OC), 38, 87
octyl methoxycinnamate (octinoxate,
   OMC), 31, 37-38, 46-48,
   71, 78-79, 91, 103, 106,
   See cinnamates
Octyl salicylate (octisalate), 38
olfactory bulbs, 61, 67, 84
osteomalacia, 94
osteoporosis, 93
oxidative stress, 44, 50, 54, 57-58,
   65, 67-68, 75
oxybenzophenone (BP3, BP2), 31,
   37-42, 45, 47-50, 66, 71-72,
   75, 78-79, 88, 90, 101-106

oxygen, 76, 102

P

PABA, 31, 38, 79, 91, 102
Padimate O, 38
palpitations (heart), 77
pancreas, 94
parathyroid, 94
Parkinson's disease, 60, 69, 81-82,
   90, 93
Parsol 1789, 44
pharmaceuticals, 43
   companies, 35
phenylbenzimidazole sulfonic acid
   (ensulizole), 38
*Photochemical & Photobiological
   Sciences,* 56
phosphorus, 93-94
photoaging, 113
phytoplankton, 105-106
phototoxicity, 105
pituitary, 71, 78
placenta, 56, 64-6, 68, 71, 84, 102
plastics, 39, 43
polycyclic musk fragrances, 71
polyphenols, 109
population,
   USA, 41, 46, 76, 83, 85, 95
   World-wide, 34
pregnancy, 44, 59-60, 64, 67-68, 73
preservatives, 71, 103
progesterone, 46, 71
propyl paraben (PP), 71
protozoa, 50
prostate, 44, 63, 65, 78, 80, 89
puberty, 48, 63, 80
   female, 63

Q

quercetin, 65

R

races,
    Blacks, 25-27
    White, 25-27, 109
reptiles, 39
rats, 44, 47-48, 57, 61, 63, 64, 67-68,
    77-78, 84-85
reactive oxygen species *See* (ROS)
reproduction, 23, 39-40, 44-46, 48,
    63-5, 71-72, 91, 98, 104
rickets, xviii, 93-94
rivers, 102
ROS (reactive oxygen species), 57-
    58, 75, 77, 81, 89
trihalomethanes, 91

S

Schiestl, Robert, 123
Science of the Total Environment,
    101
semen quality, 24
serotonin, 85
sexual development, 63, 72-73, 126
sexually dimorphic brain
    development, 72-73
Shanghai, 105
Shukla, R.K., 52
skin, 23-5, 27-31, 37-8, 40-41, 60,
    93-95, 98, 101, 109, 117,
    122, 123-125
    aging, 58, 75, 119, 125
    cancer, 23-7, 30-3, 43-44, 49-
        50, 95, 106, 110, 117-
        119, 121
    penetration, 47, 56, 59

solar radiation, 23, 27-32, 37, 50, 75,
    80, 95, 109-110
Spain, 102
sperm (count/quality), 44, 53, 63, 65
SPF (Solar Protective Factor), 37,
    50, 58, 69, 110, 118-119,
    125
spleen, 47, 61
spray-on tan, 61, 80-81, 121
squamous cell carcinoma, 25, 121
statin drugs, 107
stilbenes, 109
sulisobenzone (BP4), 38
sun allergies, 122
sun protective clothing, 31, 33, 40,
    99, 110, 117-119, 122, 124-
    125
    SPF rated, 110
sunburn, 27-8, 30, 32, 34, 49, 59,
    119, 124-125
Sunscreen Biohazard: Treat as
    Hazardous Waste, 110
swimming pools, 91-92

T

T3 (triodothyronine), 71, 78
T4 (thyroxine), 44, 71, 78
tanning salons, 121
teratogenicity, 40
testicles, 47, 53, 65, 78, 110
    fetal, 72
    sperm quality, 65
testosterone, 44, 65, 73, 78, 98
    anti-testosterone, 72-73, 104
    receptors, 39, 46, 71
thyroid, 46, 63, 88, 94
    receptors, 25-27, 39, 46
thyroid disrupting chemicals (TDCs),
    23, 71, 78
thyroid hormones, 39, 44, 46, 63, 71

thyroid stimulating hormone (TSH), 78
thyroxine (T4), *See* T4
titanium dioxide (TiO2), 26, 37-38, 51-59, 61, 64-68, 77, 84-86, 88-90, 98, 101, 110, 123-125
   anatase, 58-59, 68
   brain, 84
   Bulk vs. NPs, 54-56
   candy, 53
   chewing gum, 53
   "Kid Safe", 51, 53, 81
   lacquers, 53
   paints, 53
   pudding, 53
   rutile, 58
   seafood, 66
   tooth paste, 53
   See also nanoparticles
tocopherols, 109
tocotrienols, 109
total sunshine, 24
toxicity, 39-40, 42, 48, 52, 54, 56, 58, 60, 63-6, 71, 75-77, 85, 87, 89, 98, 102, 106
Toxicity Report Series, 47
triiodothyronine (T3), *See* T3
Trolamine salicylate, 38

U

ultraviolet (UV). *See* UV
United States (U.S.), 25, 34, 40-41, 57
   BP3 in population, 49
   Environmental Protection Agency (EPA), 111
   FDA approved chemicals, 38, 45-6, 65, 106
   melanoma incidence, 26

University of California, San Diego, 95
U.S. *See* United States
U.S. Centers for Disease Control and Prevention (CDC), 40-41
United States National Biomonitoring Program, 40
urine, 49
U.S. National Weather Service, 120
U.S. Virgin Islands, 104
uteri, 68
uterus, 64, 71, 78
UV (ultraviolet), 27, 31, 37, 41-42, 45, 58-59, 75, 109
   filters, 24, 34, 37-39, 37-50, 66, 75, 79, 91, 101, 105
UVA, 24, 26-9, 34, 38, 44, 51, 58, 97, 119
UVB, 24, 26-28, 34, 38, 51, 80, 82-84, 94-95, 97, 110, 119
UV Index Rating System, 120

V

vagina, 71, 78
Virgin Islands, 104
vitamin A, 186
vitamin C, 150, 181, 191, 196, 232, 236
vitamin D, 23, 80, 83, 93-99, 110, 117, 121

W

wastewater treatment plants, 101
water (ground/tap), 102
White (Caucasians). *See* races, White

X

Z

zinc oxide (ZnO), 26, 37-38, 51-53,
          55-61, 64-66, 75-77, 80-90,
          101, 104-106, 123
     bacterial flora, 80
     "Kid Safe", 51, 53, 81
     See also nanoparticles

About the Authors

Elizabeth Plourde, C.L.S., NCMP, Ph.D.
Clinical Laboratory Scientist
NAMS Certified Menopause Practitioner
Medical Researcher
Health Coach
Author

International lecturer and author of health books, Dr. Plourde is a licensed Clinical Laboratory Scientist (CLS) and North American Menopause Society Certified Menopause Practitioner, whose career included working with cutting-edge cancer and DNA medical research laboratories. The author's well-rounded education and professional expertise provided the background necessary to research the scientific and medical literature to compile this vital-to-know information in an understandable format.

Her 30-years of research and expertise in the field of health have resulted in presentations at medical conferences and on numerous network news and TV and radio shows.

Marcus Plourde, Ph.D.
21st Century Health Consulting LLC

As Editor-in-Chief of New Voice Publications, Dr. Plourde has spent two decades conducting medical research. New Voice offers books, educational services, and consulting that promote good health and treat the root causes of disease, rather than treating symptoms. In the process of editing and publishing cutting-edge alternative and holistic health books, it became apparent that consumers are not receiving the best health care available from *standard of care* medicine. It is New Voice Publication's mission to provide the educational resources consumers need to become their own advocates and take active roles in their health care choices.

Made in the USA
Las Vegas, NV
17 July 2022

51643766R00095